Introduction to the study of soils in tropical and subtropical regions

D1547010

The author is Professor of Tropical Soil Science at the Agricultural University, Wageningen, the Netherlands

Introduction to the study of soils in tropical and subtropical regions

P.Buringh

3rd edition

Wageningen
Centre for Agricultural Publishing and Documentation
1979

First published 1968
Second edition 1970 (revised)
Third edition 1979 (revised)

ISBN 90-220-0691-3

Contents

Preface to the third edition

This book is written for young soil scientists and specialists in related subjects who are interested in soils of the tropics and subtropics, and in their evaluation for agricultural use. It is an introduction, dealing with general aspects of major soils. The reader is supposed to have a basic knowledge of soil science.

The first edition of this introduction was published in 1968. A second edition (1970) was reprinted several times and was translated in Japanese and Turkish. This third edition is reorganized and rewritten because knowledge of tropical soils has much increased. Terminology and nomenclature have changed drastically. Since there are some excellent textbooks on tropical soils and on special subjects, I decided not to describe details but to concentrate on general aspects of major soils, particularly of tropical regions. The nomenclature developed for the recently published 'Soil Map of the World' by FAO/Unesco has been used, because the names of major soils on the world map have been adopted in several tropical countries. A special chapter deals with the new US soil classification system called 'Soil Taxonomy'. Soil names commonly used in older publications are mentioned in a glossary together with the approximately equivalent names of major soils as used in this book.

In all chapters, a choice had to be made whether a particular subject should be dealt with or omitted. I realize that some colleagues might have other preferences. This introduction is a compilation of knowledge and experience of some generations of soil scientists throughout the world. I did not mention them in the text, because it is hardly possible to give individual authors credit in an introductory book. Reference is made only to bibliographies, and to generally available books and reports that are interesting for those who want to learn more about various subjects.

I wish to express my great appreciation to all soil scientists who have sent me remarks and who have encouraged me to work on a completely new edition. Suggestions for improvements are again welcome.

Wageningen, March, 1979

1

1 Land use

1.1 Land area and its productive capacity

The land area of our planet is 14.8 thousand million hectares (148 million square kilometres). It is 29% of the earth's surface, 71% being water. About 1.4 thousand million hectares of land is permanently covered by ice and 13.4 thousand million hectares is really land. This is used as indicated in Table 1.

The category 'other land' is mainly tundra land in polar regions, arid land in deserts and stony and rocky land in mountains. It also includes 400 million hectares of land occupied by houses, industries, roads and airports. According to recent studies, 25% of the land area is suitable for cultivation, that is some 3400 million hectares. Most reserves are in Africa and Latin America.

Table 1. General land use of the world (1975). Source: FAO, Production Yearbook 1975.

	Area (million ha)	Proportion of land surface (%)
Arable land	1 507	11.3
Grass land	3 044	22.7
Forest land	4 053	30.3
Other land	4 788	35.7
World total land	13 392	

The tropics, being defined as the part of the world between the Tropic of Cancer and the Tropic of Capricorn, comprise some 5 thousand million hectares or 38% of the land surface. The subtropics are the regions north and south of the tropics up to about 35° latitude. The boundaries with the temperate regions are not well defined. The land area of the subtropics may be estimated at some 25% of the total land surface.

There is some 1 386 million km^3 of water on our planet, 96.5% is in oceans, and only 2.53% is fresh water. Of this 69% is in glaciers and snow, 30% in groundwater, and less than 1% in rivers, lakes and swamps. The annual water discharge by all rivers is estimated at 44 500 km^3. A part of it is used to irrigate 205 million hectares of agricultural land. It is expected that this area can be extended to a total of 400 million hectares, taking into account that human and industrial use of fresh water will increase as well.

Calculations have been made of the primary production of the biosphere, that is the binding of sunlight energy into organic matter by plants that support all life. The net annual primary production (production minus the material used for respiration) is estimated at 172 gigatonnes (172×10^{12} kg) of organic matter of which 117 gigatonnes are produced on land. The net annual primary production is high in tropical rain forests (20 t.ha.$^{-1}$; 2 kg.m^{-2}), and it is on average 6 t.ha^{-1} on arable land. It is estimated that the total net primary production on land is at present only some 70% of what it was in the remote past, when there were no people. The main reason for this decrease is the felling and destruction of large areas of forests since early prehistoric times.

1.2 Land-use constraints

Not all land can be used for agricultural purposes because production is limited by unfavourable conditions of climate, topography, hydrology or soils. Biological production is only possible if at least minimum requirements are met. This also holds for crops. Some conditions can be improved by man, for instance by irrigation, terracing, drainage or deep ploughing. Besides physical constraints, there are often social, economic or political constraints to agricultural production. For instance, many farmers are poor and illiterate or there is no infrastructure or no market for products; the government can fix prices of products. Socio-economic and political constraints are often more important than physical constraints. They are, however, not subjects for this book.

For climate, important factors are soil temperature, precipitation and solar radiation. Soils can be classified according to their temperature and moisture regimes (Section 4.5). This is a rather recent improvement, because similar soils with different temperature regimes have quite different potentialities for agricultural use. Precipitation is an important factor, both for agricultural production and for soil information. In 70% of land in the tropics and probably 80% in the subtropics, precipitation is a limiting factor for crop production. Rainfall in the driest part of the world is almost zero, whereas the maximum precipitation in the wettest part of the tropics is more than 10 m per year. In large parts of the tropics and subtropics, wet and dry seasons alternate. A dry season in the tropics is defined by the number of dry months (< 100 mm rainfall). For semi-arid regions, there is a difference in agricultural potential between regions having rainfall in the cold or in the warm season, because of difference in evapotranspiration. The length of day (the time be-

3

tween sunrise and sunset) is an important factor for various crops.

These factors are important for land use. For details see the various textbooks. Soil conditions are discussed below.

1.3 Land use and soil conditions

If environmental conditions for growing crops are favourable, soil conditions often limit production. The main limiting soil factors are shallow soil, presence of many stones or rock outcrops, high groundwater table, low water-holding capacity, poor internal drainage, slow soil permeability, low soil fertility, low cation-exchange capacity, presence of toxic ions or highly soluble salts, and absence of minor nutritional elements. There are major variations in these and other soil properties and qualities, and consequently some soils are more suitable for crops than others. Some limiting factors can be improved by appropriate farm management. Most familiar is the application of fertilizers to improve the nutrient status of soils.

Under natural conditions, vegetation is adapted to the environment. Large areas in the world, even in remote parts of the tropics, are influenced by the activity of man, who has always selected regions most suitable for living conditions. Essential for him are availability of drinking water, of soils suitable to collect or grow food, and of wood for cooking meals and making a shelter. River valleys, deltas and volcanic regions with enough rainfall and a favourable temperature are the most suitable places and consequently most people live there. Those who had to live in a less favourable environment, where natural fertility of soils was limited, could live only by cultivating land for a few years followed by shifting to new land, which was generally forest. Several types of shifting cultivation have been developed and some 200 million people still depend on this type of farming in an area of 3000 million hectare of forest. So about 5 ha of land is needed per person. It takes 10 to 12 years before the land that has been cultivated for some years can be used again. A large area per person is also needed by people depending on livestock, particularly in semi-arid areas, where grass grows only during a few rainy months. Under more favourable environmental, especially soil conditions, permanent cultivation of land is possible and one hectare of land can feed several persons.

These examples demonstrate that land use depends closely on soil conditions, even when other conditions are favourable. All types of constraints considered, tropical and sub-tropical regions are only partly suitable for agricultural production, not only under natural environmental conditions but also when advanced techniques of farming are introduced.

1.4 Agricultural use of land

About 11% of the land area in the world is cultivated land. In areas with pronounced and long dry seasons, crops are grown once in three years, whereas under highly favourable conditions two or three crops can be grown annually. Grassland is found on 22% of the land area. Part of this grassland produces 20 tonnes of dry matter per hectare (2 kg.m^{-2}); other land that is less productive does not produce more than 1 t.ha.$^{-1}$.

Real desert produces hardly anything at all. About half of the tropical land and probably a quarter of the subtropical land is forest of different type and quality. It supplies firewood, timber, and pulp for the paper industry. In the tropics, some 80% of all wood cut is used as fire wood. In areas with a pronounced dry season where vegetation is rather scarce, most trees are cut for firewood and hardly any trees are left. In the real tropical forests, suitable trees are cut at ever-increasing rate both for export and local needs. Relative to reforestation, felling of forests is tremendous. A few years ago, felling of forest trees in the world's last large tropical forest reserve in the Amazon river basin started. It is estimated that, within 25 years, half of this forest will be cut down.

Agricultural production of tropical land is low. Various systems of low-yielding traditional and subsisting farming are in common use, except in special plantations and in some more advanced regions such as river deltas as of the Nile. It has been proved in several countries that production on cultivated land and on grassland can be tremendously increased. Unfortunately preference is often given to reclamation of new land, since the population is increasing rapidly and much more food is needed. However a slightly improved system of agriculture on all the land cultivated now might solve all food problems. The main food crops in the tropics are paddy (2.0 t.ha^{-1}), cassava (9.4 t.ha^{-1}), maize (1.2 t.ha^{-1}), wheat (1.2 t.ha^{-1}), sorghum (0.7 t.ha^{-1}) and millet (0.5 t.ha^{-1}). The average yields are low, particularly when compared with average yields obtained in areas with improved management, were yields may be 3 to 7 times as high. Cereal grains, occupying 66% of all cultivated land in the world, produce 75% of all human food (proportion by dry weight). Only 20% of all cereal land in the world gets fertilizers. In the tropics, the proportion is much lower.

The average grassland yields are very low too. In the tropics and subtropics, an average of 5 kg beef is produced per hectare. Only 3% of all grassland in the world gets fertilizers.

In most subtropical countries, the situation is somewhat better, management is somewhat more advanced but productivity can easily be improved

5

too, at least its technical aspect. The socio-economic and political conditions in many countries do not encourage poor farmers to increase production, because extra investment lines the pockets of money lenders, land owners or pump owners. Poor farmers should not be blamed. They often produce more per hectare than rich farmers do. Although it is no part of soil science, land ownership must be mentioned. It is not always realized that most land in many countries is owned by a few people. In the advanced countries in the northern hemisphere, the grip of 'agribusiness' on agriculture is ever increasing. A similar situation is expected for the tropics.

1.5 Non-agricultural use of land

Non-agricultural uses of land include housing, traffic, industry, open-cast mining and recreation. The area is expanding since population is increasing rapidly. In some countries, 0.1 to 0.5% of the good cultivated land is lost each year for these purposes. Most cities, towns and villages lie on the best soils and therefore more land of the best land classes is lost. Since it is expected that the world population will double in 35 years, everybody can foresee what will happen in the near future.

1.6 Misuse of land

Large areas of agricultural land are lost because of soil erosion, soil salinization, alkalization, and desertification. The rate of loss is estimated at 600-900 ha.h^{-1}, that is 5-8 million hectare per year. These losses could be prevented, because all the technical knowledge and experience needed is available. Misuse of agricultural land is a very serious problem.

1.7 The task of the soil scientist

A soil scientist has to deal with many problems. These are not only problems of soil science, of which many still have to be solved. He also has to deal with various other more general problems, such as those reviewed in this chapter. Neither he nor all soil scientists together can solve the many social and political problems. Soil scientists and other specialists should be aware of their responsibility to inform authorities on land-use potentials, and on possible choices. Every soil scientist has also the task of supplying data and results of his work in such a way that they can be used in planning and execution of projects. Many current problems are associated with land use.

Selected literature: Vink (1974); Whyte (1976).

2 Soil science

2.1 History

Each farmer knows his land and its soils by experience. Knowledge of soils is as old as mankind. More than hundred years ago, Dokuchajev, a Russian soil scientist, started a systematic study of soils. He discovered the geographic distribution of soils in relation to climatic zones, and became the founder of soil science. Major progress was made after chemistry was developed and applied to soils and plant growth (Liebig). Chemical fertilizers were introduced. Soil research in tropical countries started later. It is still interesting to read early publications on tropical soils by Mohr (Indonesia), Baeyens (Zaire), Hardy (Trinidad) and others. After 1945, there was a stagnation in the development of tropical soil research, caused by the transition of many countries to independence, but later soil studies were encouraged, particularly by the International Soil Science Society (ISSS) and by the Food and Agricultural Organization (FAO) of the United Nations. FAO together with Unesco has prepared a 'Soil Map of the World', scale 1:5 000 000, for which many soil scientists have cooperated. This work has acted as a stimulant, and during the last decade much progress has been made.

Beside the book on tropical soils by Mohr and van Baren (1954; 3rd edition by Mohr et al. 1972), which was the first book on this subject, there are now three other textbooks (Section 2.3). There are various chapters on tropical soils in books on agriculture and many articles in journals of soil science. Knowledge of soils in the tropics and subtropics is increasing rapidly. Many tropical and some of the subtropical soils have quite different properties, qualities, characteristics and potentialities from the much better studied soils of temperate regions. Often knowledge and experience with soils of the Northern Hemisphere cannot be transferred to soils of the tropics and consequently a special branch of soil science was developed, often called 'tropical soil science'.

Each soil has specific properties, qualities and characteristics. It occupies a small three-dimensional part of the land surface. It can be recognized in the field and its position can be indicated on a map, a soil map. Such a soil map shows several soils, which are given names. After some years of soil investigation and mapping, so many soils have been investigated, that they have to be grouped and classified. Different countries have classified their soils in different ways, so there are many systems of soil classification (Section 2.5).

To investigate biological, chemical, physical and mineralogical properties, different laboratories use different methods. The many books on soil analysis offer different methods whose results are unfortunately often almost impossible to compare.

It is extremely difficult to understand how soils have formed (soil genesis) and to know the processes leading to formation of soils. Problems related to this subject are mostly studied from a chemical or physical, and less from a biological or biochemical point of view. Soil microbiology is attracting somewhat more attention.

Soil management, improvement and reclamation include aspects of soil science that also are studied by specialists in these disciplines.

A 'Committee on Tropical Soils' (1972) has reported on the research needs of tropical soils. There is hardly any article or book that does not suggest the need for more research. However there is at present much knowledge and experience that could be applied. If this were done on all agricultural land in the tropics and subtropics, many problems, including that of world food shortage, could be solved and there would be no need for reclamation of new land.

2.2 Branches

Soils are used mainly for agricultural production to supply food, clothes and wood for the world population. As there are many soils and many major regional differences in soil condition, agronomists are interested in knowledge of soils in order to help farmers in solving their cropping problems. In addition, experts in land reclamation, biologists, plant geographers, geomorphologists, geographers, and all those interested in earth sciences also study soils.

As each soil has specific chemical, physical, biological and mineralogical properties, specialists in these sciences devote much time to studying these properties. Much research has been done and many details have been investigated in some soils. Each year, some 7000 articles on many subjects are published. There are many types of soil scientist with different background, education and knowledge for a specific part of soil science. The International Soil Science Society therefore has seven commissions dealing with particular branches of soil science (soil physics, soil chemistry, soil biology, soil fertility and plant nutrition, soil genesis, classification and cartography, soil technology, and soil mineralogy).

Some soil scientists work on problems in order to increase knowledge; some try to apply results in practice; some do both. Soil science has extended so fast that it is impossible for one scientist to be competent in all branches. In most countries, a team of specialists works in soil institutes and university departments. None of them should forget that real soils are in the field, and that soils are an indispensable medium to grow food for people and animals and to support natural vegetation.

2.3 Literature

Soil scientists are fortunate, because literature on all aspects of soil science is collected and published with a short abstract in a monthly journal 'Soils and Fertilizers', prepared by the Commonwealth Bureau of Soils of the Commonwealth Agricultural Bureaux, Farnham Royal, Slough SL2 3BN, in the United Kingdom. In 1979, Volume 42 was published. In addition, the Commonwealth Bureau of Soils also publishes annotated bibliographies on various subjects, including bibliographies on soils of various countries.

A special 'Bibliography of the Soils of the Tropics' is being published as Technical Series Bulletin No 17 by the Office of Agriculture, Technical Assistance Bureau, Agency for International Development, Washington, DC 20523 in the United States of America.

There are four textbooks on tropical soils: Mohr et al. (1972), Kalpagé (1976), Sanchez (1976), and Young (1976). These books are useful for further reading and study.

The oldest is that of Mohr et al. (1972, 3rd edition), which was first written by Mohr and van Baren (1954). It is based mainly on knowledge and experience of soils in Indonesia. It has extensive chapters on soil-forming factors and the various processes of soil formation. There is also a chapter on paddy (rice) soils and one on theoretical considerations of basic dynamics of weathering and soil formation. Old and new American names of soils are used.

Kalpagé's book (1976) is a more general one, dealing with the main tropical soils (old American names), their nutrient supply, fertility and use. It has a glossary of 24 pages.

The book by Sanchez (1976) does not deal with soil genesis and the processes of soil development, but concentrates on soil management. It is valuable for those who want to know more about agricultural potential of tropical soils, fertility and application of fertilizers. Soil management in shifting cultivation areas, in rice cultivation, in multiple cropping and for pastures are discussed. Much information is on Latin American soils. Sanchez devotes a short chapter to various soil classification systems and uses the new American system of soil classification and nomenclature throughout (Chapter 6).

Young (1976) concentrates on soil information, tropical soils, their classification and evaluation, soil fertility, soil survey and land evaluation. Most of his information is on soils of Africa. It is written from a point of view of a field soil scientist. The nomenclature is mainly that used in various soil classifications in African countries, but reference is also made to the soil units of the FAO/Unesco Soil Map of the World.

These books are valuable on tropical soils. They are written from different approaches and are consequently complementary. They all have long lists of selected literature.

In this introduction, reference is made only to books in English. However almost half of the important literature on tropical soils is in French, and there is some literature in Spanish and Portuguese too. The French literature is mainly published by ORSTOM, the oversea's scientific and technical research organization at Paris, and by INEAC (the national institute for agronomic studies in the Congo, now Zaire) at Brussels. At the end of the list of selected literature, a short list is given of publications in French. The concepts and terminology in French are quite different from those in English.

A number of books deal with specific tropical or subtropical soils; some are mentioned later. Other books and proceedings of conferences and symposia also deal with special subjects of soil science and its application. Attention must be drawn also to Volumes I-X belonging to the Soil Map of the World (FAO/Unesco, 1971-1978), dealing with the soils of the various continents. They include many references and are written in two of the four following languages English, French, Russian and Spanish, according to the languages most used in the continents. In each volume (except Volume I, Legend), a number of soils are described in detail together with analytical data.

2.4 Study of soils

Soils and their environmental conditions are studied in the field in relation to plant growth. Pits to a depth of 1.5 m or more are dug and soil profiles are examined in the walls of these pits. Special attention is paid to the properties of surface layers (20 cm), presence and distribution of plant roots, layers or horizons, their characteristics and thickness, soil organic matter, soil porosity, and the influence of ground water. When several soil pits, equally distributed over an area to be investigated, have been carefully examined, the soil profiles are compared and it is decided which soil units have to be distinguished, and which pits represent the typical characteristics of these soil units. The pits are again examined and a complete description is made of the profiles. Soil samples of the various layers or horizons are taken for examination in a laboratory. The typical characteristics of each soil unit and the differences from other soils are described. More pits or auger holes are made and the boundaries of each soil unit are determined and drawn on a map or aerial photograph. Aerial photo-interpretation may help to decide where to dig pits and how to find and draw boundaries between soil units. If there are clear differences in vegetation or in growth of crops, soil profiles should be studied and compared at spots where crops grow best and where they grow worst, in order to trace reasons for differences in crop growth.

The procedure is more elaborate than described above. Soils must be examined by a specific procedure, and described according to uniform definitions, terminology and nomenclature. These are described in soil survey manuals, mainly the manuals of the US Soil Survey Staff (1951), of which a new edition is in preparation, FAO (1977) or national manuals. Various books describe the procedures to be followed when analysing soil samples. The manuals mentioned above indicate what procedures are preferred.

2.5 Classification of soils

Classification of soils is a controversial subject, both national and international, because soil scientists often do not agree on the soil properties to be used to distinguish and to classify soils. Consequently definitions and nomenclature are different. Reviews of various systems of soil classification are given in most books of soil science. During the last decade, all systems of soil classification have changed, because they had to be improved since knowledge of soils is rapidly increasing. The new system of soil classification by the US Soil Survey Staff (1975) 'Soil Taxonomy' (Chapter 6) is the best and most comprehensive system. It was established in cooperation with soil scientists in various countries all over the world. It is rather complicated, and one needs thorough training to handle it. It is a 'morphometric' system: in other words, that all properties used to characterize soils can be measured in the field or in the laboratory. Soils are classified according to the presence or absence of such properties. In practical soil investigations, 'Soil Taxonomy' has the disadvantage that many soils can only be classified after various laboratory tests. This can be done usually only for reference soil profiles (benchmark soils).

Systematic systems of soil classification have been developed in order to arrange soils in various classes (taxa) that can be easily remembered. Soils can then be compared and knowledge and experience of soils in one region can be applied elsewhere with similar properties and environmental conditions. It is hardly possible to collect soils in the way biologists collect plants in an herbarium. Very often soil monoliths (thin soil profiles, fixed on hardboard and preserved with plastics) are made and brought together in order to facilitate comparison. Most national soil survey institutes have such a collection of soil monoliths. The recently established 'International Soil Museum' at Wageningen in the Netherlands, founded by the Dutch Government in cooperation with the International Soil Science Society and Unesco, is setting up an international collection of soils.

The names given to similar soils are often different, firstly because of differences in languages and secondly because of the different criteria of soil classification. Some names are applied to several kinds of soil. There has been and still is much confusion in soil science, often even within one country. Completely artificial names have been introduced in 'Soil Taxonomy'.

It is important to have a uniform terminology and a consistent soil classification, at least within one country. Descriptions of soils have to be made according to a uniform system and soil has to be analysed according to standard methods. Much work has already been done in this field.

It is not necessary to apply a systematic system of soil classification when a soil survey of a region has to be carried out. Mostly it is even better not to do so, at least in semi-detailed and more general investigations. During a soil survey, all soils of an area are studied intensively and in detail, and it is learned which soil properties are important and which soil properties of the various soils differ. It depends on the purpose of a soil survey which and how many properties are used to separate and to characterize the soil units shown on a soil map. These soil units, often called soil mapping units, are listed in the legend of the soil map. This is also soil classification, because here too soils are classified according to specific soil properties. Soil maps are made for specific purposes, for instance to know the suitability of soils for crops, their potential for crops, choice of land use, scope for improvement, for drainage or for reclamation. For almost every purpose, quite different criteria are needed to characterize the soil units of a soil map. So different soil maps can be made of the same region, depending on the purpose of the soil survey. A soil map made for one purpose is not necessarily suitable for another purpose. In practical soil survey, the soil units are therefore classified with a view to the purpose of the soil investigation. Simultaneously data are collected for a systematic classification of soils in a country.

Soil investigations and classifications are made at several levels of generalization. In general investigations and reconnaissance surveys, only the main differences in soils can be presented on rather small scale maps. Such maps may have a similar legend for various regions with similar soils. For semi-detailed and particularly for detailed investigations, legends of surveyed soil units are often different, depending on the purpose of the investigation.

The 'Soil Map of the World' recently published by FAO/Unesco (1971-1978) shows the major soils of the world as they occur in the various continents and can be depicted on a map with a scale 1:5 000 000. Only the major soils can be indicated, because a quarter of a square centimetre of the map, wich is the smallest unit that can be shown separately, represents an area of 6250 ha (62.5 km²). A soil that occupies an area of 1000 or of 5000 ha cannot be shown on this map. Consequently the map shows only the presence and position of major soils, being associations of various soils, combined in general soil units. The legend of the Soil Map of the World shows how soils are classified and named. The reports describe the major soils, their properties and characteristics.

For an explanation of the difference between the soil classification of 'Soil Taxonomy' and that of the 'Soil Map of the World' (and of most other soil maps), reference can be made to biology. There are millions of plant species (like soils). They have been systematically classified in a flora (Soil Taxonomy) that enables us to determine according to various properties each species of plant (kind of soil). In plant geography, the purpose is to find out which plants (soils) are present in the field and where they occur. Everywhere, several species of plants (soils) occur in an association at the same site. Plant geographers (soil surveyors), who want to indicate on maps the occurrence and position (boundaries) of the plants, will make a map showing the various plant associations (soil associations).

In wet depressions, on well-drained slopes and on hill tops, they will find quite different associations of plants that are mapped separately after they have determined which plants are characteristic for each association.

'Soil Taxonomy' and other systems of soil classification are the 'floras' of soil science. Soil maps show units of soils in their geographic position. Principles of classification are different. In very detailed surveys and in areas with uniform soil conditions, soils can sometimes be shown according to the most detailed category of a systematic classification. Normally this is hardly possible.

It is still proving difficult for many countries to decide which system of soil classification to use. Even political reasons have influenced decisions. The main point is that soil classifications for soil mapping have to be set up in such a way that they serve the purpose of soil investigation. Another point is that there is also a need for a complete collection of descriptions of all soils of a country for which a systematic system of soil classification has to be developed or adopted. In each country, the responsible officials should decide themselves. It is unwise not to exploit all knowledge and experience that is already available in countries with a long tradition in soil classification.

2.6 Soil survey, soil maps and reports

For some purposes, a detailed or very detailed investigation of soils is needed and many field observations (profile pits and soil augerings) have to be made in each soil unit. For other purposes, only the main differences in soil conditions need be mapped, and fewer field observations made. For the latter, however, the less detailed soil map has to be based on detailed soil studies in some 'sample areas', small areas in the project area representing typical conditions. For some purposes, only a general view of soil conditions is needed, and a very general soil map can be made. Generally it is not necessary to spent much time in studying soils in areas considered unsuitable for the purpose of the survey.

Different types of soil maps can be made, for instance very detailed, detailed, semi-detailed, reconnaissance, general and exploratory. The soil survey report indicates how many field observations have been made per unit area. As the smallest area to be shown on a soil map should have at least one field observation, this area can be determined. On the other hand, if it is known what the smallest area to be shown on the map is, then the minimum number of field observations can be calculated. This determines the scale of a soil map.

Soil boundaries are indicated as accurately as possible, with respect to the scale of the soil map. Some boundaries are real clear boundaries, others represent transitional zones. Each soil map is accompanied by a report. Such a report is important for soil scientists and sometimes even more so for other specialists, who have to be informed on soil conditions in order to do their job. So it is necessary that separate chapters deal, for instance, with how to use a soil map and report, and describe in a rather simple way general soil conditions, the main soils, and the main conclusions. Often special maps are made for particular soil phenomena or for soil suitability or soil potentialities for specific land use. The report also has to describe why soil analyses are made, what the results are and how they have to be interpreted. A final remark is that many soil surveyors make too many auger holes and not enough pits. Next to each auger hole a shallow pit some 30 or 40 cm deep can easily be made. They give important information.

2.7 Soil Map of the World

The FAO/Unesco (1971-1978) Soil Map of the World is a compilation of all soil maps available (FAO, 1973). All maps had to be translated in order to get a uniform result. Soils that are geographically related were combined in soil associations called 'major soils'. These major soils, 106 in total, are shown separately or in combination. Some special properties are indicated by extra symbols. In the Legend of the Soil Map of the World (Sheet I, Volume I), the major soils are shown under 16 headings. It has been a tremendous work for the soil staff of FAO in cooperation with leading soil specialists of almost all countries of the world to prepare this map. The result is excellent. For the first time there is a real Soil Map of the World. Of course, there are some mistakes and shortcomings, mainly because soils in large areas of the world (almost 80%) remain to be investigated. Soil maps are available only for limited areas of many countries. Small maps show the reliability of the soil map. The new soil map is particularly useful for agriculture because for most soil units suitability for agriculture under traditional and improved management is indicated. The scale of the map, 1:5 000 000, establishes limitations. The map gives only a general and global idea about the 'major soils' of the world.

The soil classification for the Soil Map of the World is not a systematic classification of all soils of the world; it is a classification of soil mapping units. This textbook deals with the major soils in the tropics and subtropics. The major soils as described in the following chapters are those of the 'Soil Map of the World'. Much information in this textbook is available in more detail in the various volumes of the Soil Map of the World. Here the same definitions, terminology and nomenclature are used, except in Chapter 6 that deals with the United States system of 'Soil Taxonomy'. This is done for two reasons: firstly because within a few years most soil specialists will be familiar with the FAO/Unesco Soil Map of the World and its legend of major soils; secondly because it is impossible to mention all soil names used in countries where tropical and subtropical soils have been investigated. For readers of this book, it would be too confusing. Many older soil names are listed in the glossary (Appendix). A special glossary of soil science terms is published by the Soil Science Society of America (1978).

The major soils of the world are shown in more than 5000 map units. Some soil specialists have taken the legend of the Soil Map of the World as a system of soil classification that can be used in all countries of the world. Here two mistakes are made. The first is that there are more soils in the world than those 106 'major soils' and that it is not a systematic classification like 'Soil Taxonomy'. Secondly it is doubtful whether soils in a particular area to be investigated occur in similar associations as are indicated on the Soil Map of the World. It surely is necessary to add many details if soils are to be mapped on a larger scale. It would be possible to add such details and to develop a soil map legend with various subdivisions of each major soil but that has not been done. If it is to be done in the future, there will surely be many different opinions, because there will be no consensus about the purpose for which such a map is made. The next step might be a new soil map of the world of scale 1:1 000 000, based on sufficient investigations of potential agricultural land, particularly cultivated land. The present legend of major soils can be expanded.

2.8 General characteristics of groups of major soils

Each group of major soils as indicated on the FAO/Unesco Soil Map of the World has a set of properties in which it differs from the other groups of major soils. The main general characteristics are given below in simplified manner. Further details are presented in Chapter 3. The groups are described in a sequence that is also a key to recognize and classify soils units. As soon as a first unit is characterized, the next does not have the properties of the first one. A third group does not have the properties of the first and second, and so on. As the descriptions are simplified, the key of this section cannot be used for soil identification. This should be done with the original key. A short description of the soil horizons and properties mentioned for the various soils is given in Chapter 4.

Histosols All organic soils or peat soils with an organic layer of $\geqslant 40$ cm (all following soils are mineral soils).

Lithosols Very thin soils (< 10 cm thick) over hard rock.

Vertisols Very heavy clay soils ($\geqslant 30\%$ clay) with deep and wide cracks in the dry season, with a specific microrelief (gilgai relief), and with slickensides in the subsoil (25-100 cm). Vertisols occur in large flat clay plains, where the climate is characterized by a real dry season of some months, during which these heavy montmorillonitic clays shrink and crack. Gilgai relief and slickensides result from intensive alternating shrinkage and swelling. See Figures 1, 2 and 3.

Fluvisols Recent alluvial deposits in river valleys, deltas and coastal regions with very little soil development. Most soils consist of stratified layers with

16

different textures, because these layers consist of sediments deposited by water. Fluvisols do not have high salinity. (Contrast Solonchaks.) As these soils are young, soil profile development is still weak. See Plate 1.

Solonchaks Highly saline soils, with a high content of easily soluble salts, mainly chlorides and sulphates. Solonchaks occur in arid and semi-arid regions and often have high groundwater with a high salt content. See Plate 2.

Gleysols Soils dominated by hydromorphic properties in the zone 0-50 cm, being soils with high groundwater. (Remark: the soils developed in recent alluvial material that have hydromorphic properties are classified as Fluvisols, which are therefore mentioned before Gleysols in the key). The lower part of Gleysols is always in the groundwater and consequently anaerobic and in a permanent stage of reduction, whereas, in the zone of fluctuating ground-water, reduction and oxidation alternate. The result is mobilization (reduction) and immobilization (oxidation) of iron compounds, causing a mottling of that soil zone, which develops hydromorphic properties. See Plate 3.

Andosols Soils consisting of volcanic ash or formed in volcanic ash material, often with a thick dark upper horizon. As volcanic ash is light material, the bulk density is very low (<0.85 g.cm^{-3}). Bulk density of normal mineral soils is generally 1.4 to 1.6 g.cm^{-3}. See Plate 4.

Arenosols Coarse-textured sandy soils with an ochric A horizon and in the subsoil some characteristics of an argillic, cambic or oxic B horizon, but with too sandy a soil texture. The real B horizons just mentioned are defined by a set of soil properties, and one is a limit of the soil texture class. Therefore Arenosols represent all the coarse-textured soils of some other major groups to be discussed shortly. Arenosols also include the bleached white sands, consisting of pure quartz and formed in thick tropical Podzols. See Plate 5.

Regosols Soils without soil development. There may be an ochric A horizon, indicating a weak soil surface horizon development, for example in sands of desert areas.

Rankers Soils with a dark (umbric) A horizon not more than 25 cm thick and developed from silicious parent material.

Rendzinas Soils with a dark (mollic) A horizon not more than 25 cm thick and developed from calcareous parent material.

Before continuing with the other groups of major soils it is necessary to realize what has been done so far, because all other groups to be discussed below are quite different, as they are more developed. Above all, groups of major soils with deviant characteristics have been distinguished from the others. Firstly the organic soils (Histosols) were distinguished from the mineral soils. Of all mineral soils, those with a very thin soil layer (Lithosols) were classed in one group. The other groups also have specific characteristics. Vertisols are a typical group of heavy cracking clay soils in regions with a long dry season; Fluvisols are soils in recent alluvial deposits; Solonchaks are highly saline; Gleysols have high groundwater; Andosols have a particular parent material (volcanic ash); Arenosols are sandy with some soil development; Regosols have no soil development; and Rankers and Rendzinas are rather shallow soils respectively in non-calcareous and in calcareous (limestone) material.

Podzols Heavily bleached sandy soils with a spodic B horizon in which the leached (eluviated) humus or sesquioxides or both are concentrated. In the humid tropics, they occur in regions with quartz sand. See Plate 6.

Ferralsols Deep, rather uniformly red, yellowish-red or yellow tropical soils consisting of sesquioxides and kandite (kaolinitic) clay with a low cation-exchange capacity, and an oxic B horizon. Weatherable minerals are almost absent. Physical conditions in the soils are good; chemical conditions are poor. Ferralsols are typical of the humid tropics in which hydrated oxides have accumulated. See Plate 7.

Planosols Soils with a heavily bleached light-textured surface soil over a clayey impermeable pan that is often a strong argillic or natric B horizon. Rainwater stagnates on such a clay pan; the layer above is bleached and shows hydromorphic properties. There has been severe destruction of clay in the surface layer. See Plate 8.

Solonetz Soils with a natric B horizon, being an argillic B horizon (accumulation of illuvial clay) with a high exchangeable sodium percentage (ESP $> 15\%$). Sodium clay in the upper horizons is dispersed, translocated and accumulated in the B horizon. Soil humus may be dispersed too. These soils occur mainly in semi-arid regions.

Greyzems Degraded Chernozems, being soils with a dark and rather thick A horizon (mollic) and with bleached coatings on structural elements. Not common in the tropics.

Chernozems Dark, almost black, steppe and prairie soils with organic matter accumulated to a great depth and with lime, sometimes gypsum accumulation in the subsoil. They occur mainly in semi-arid or semi-humid continental subtropical regions.

Kastanozems Dark-brown or brown steppe and prairie soils with similar characteristics to Chernozems. They occur also in semi-arid regions.

Phaeozems They have a mollic A horizon but lack horizons of lime and gypsum accumulation; some have an argillic horizon. Phaeozems have characteristics of Chernozems and Kastanozems on the one hand and of Luvisols on the other hand, and may occur in sub-humid subtropical and tropical regions.

Podzoluvisols They have a typical argillic B horizon under a bleached horizon (E horizon). Parts of this E horizon penetrate the B horizon, which therefore has an irregular or broken upper boundary. Podzoluvisols have characteristics of Podsols and Luvisols.

Xerosols They are soils of arid and semi-arid regions that are completely dry for a very long period (aridic soil moisture regime) and that have a weakly developed ochric A horizon. They mostly have only a sparse grass or bush vegetation. See Plate 9.

Yermosols They are similar to Xerosols but occur in real arid regions. They have only a very weakly developed ochric A horizon. Xerosols and Yermosols each often have horizons of calcium and gypsum accumulation. Old ones sometimes have an argillic horizon at a shallow depth.

The second group of soils shows characteristics of full soil development. In the tropics, real Podzols occur only in poor quartz material. Ferralsols are the tropical soils of humid tropics with very uniform profile development to a great depth. Planosols have an impermeable clay pan and a bleached and hydromorphic surface soil. Solonetz have a real natric B horizon. Greyzems, Kastanozems and Phaeozems are dark soils of steppes and prairies mainly in subtropical continental regions. Podzoluvisols are a type of Luvisols with clear characteristics of soil degradation. Xerosols and Yermosols are the very dry soils of semi-desert and desert areas, both in the tropics and subtropics.

Finally there are four other groups of major soils that are all important for the tropics and subtropics.

Nitosols Deep clayey, often reddish-brown, tropical soils with a diffuse argillic B horizon without plinthite, hydromorphic, ferric or vertic properties. They allow good and deep rooting, and still have weatherable minerals. Nitosols are mostly developed in basic parent material in regions without or with a short dry tropical season. They are among the best soils of the tropics. See Plate 10.

Acrisols Real old tropical outbased clay soils with a low base saturation and a distinct argillic B horizon. They occur mainly in older landtypes with a monsoon climate. See Plate 11.

Luvisols Not typical tropical soils, occurring to a large extent also in the subtropics and in temperate regions. Luvisols have an argillic B horizon, but their base saturation is high. In the tropics, they often have vertic of ferric properties, in the subtropics vertic or chromic (red colouring) properties, and in semi-arid regions accumulation of soft powdery lime. See Plates 13 and 14.

Cambisols They occur everywhere. Weathering is rather weak and there is no marked migration of weathering products. They have a cambic B horizon, being a horizon with at least a somewhat loamy texture and consisting of somewhat altered material. There may be some clay illuviation (however not enough to be an argillic horizon) or structure formation, or a somewhat redder colour, or some carbonates may be removed and accumulated in a deeper part of the soil. In the tropics, a cambic B horizon may also have ferralic or vertic properties. In general, Cambisols are mainly soils with transitional properties to the various well developed soils already mentioned, but not having the real specific properties. See Plate 15.

The last four groups of major soils consist of two real tropical soils (Nitosols and Acrisols). Luvisols and Cambisols are not typical of the tropics, but occur throughout the world.

2.9 Subdivision

Most groups of major soils of the world are subdivided according to specific properties. Below are some examples.

Gleyic Soils with hydromorphic properties within 50 cm of the surface (e.g.

Gleyic Solonchaks, Gleyic Acrisols, Gleyic Luvisols, Gleyic Cambisols).
Mollic Soils with a mollic A horizon (Mollic Andosols, Mollic Gleysols).
Humic Soils with an umbric A horizon (Humic Ferralsols).
Plinthic Soils with plinthite (Plate 12) in the zone of 0-125 cm. (Plinthic Ferralsols, Plinthic Luvisols).
Eutric Soils with base saturation more than 50% (Eutric Fluvisols, Eutric Cambisols).
Dystric Soils with base saturation less than 50% (Dystric Fluvisols, Dystric Cambisols etc). See Plate 1.
Chromic Soils with a strong brown or red B horizon (Chromic Luvisols, Chromic Cambisols). See Plate 14.
Ferralic Soils with properties of Ferralsols: a low cation-exchange capacity (Ferralic Arenosols as in Plate 5, Ferralic Cambisols).
Ferric Soils with coarse red mottles (Ferric Luvisols, Ferric Acrisols as in Plate 11).
Vertic Soils with properties of Vertisols (Vertic Luvisols, Vertic Cambisols).
Orthic Soils with the properties as described for the major soils, but not having the properties of one of the previous (Orthic Luvisols, Orthic Ferralsols) See Plate 7.
Haplic Soils with minor development of the properties of the soil group (Haplic Chernozems, Haplic Xerozems).

There are more. They are described for the relevant major soils in Chapter 3. Not all major soils occur in the tropics or subtropics, and not all soils are useful for agriculture. In the humid tropics, Andosols, Nitosols, Cambisols and Fluvisols are generally the best soils followed by Ferralsols. In the regions with a monsoon climate, Fluvisols, Vertisols and Acrisols are common and Planosols occur. Regions with a Mediterranean type of climate (cool rainy winters and dry warm summers) have Vertisols, Luvisols and Cambisols. The arid and semi-arid regions, both with a tropical and with a subtropical climate, have mainly Yermosols, Xerosols, Solonetz and Solonchaks. This is a very general indication, because some major soils occur everywhere (Fluvisols, Histosols, Cambisols, Gleysols) and in each major soil several variants occur, some with more favourable properties than others (e.g. the Eutric groups as opposed to the Dystric group, or the Orthic group as opposed to the Plinthic group). There is large variation of soils within each major soil group. Plates 1-16 show approximately the common characteristics of some major soils, and illustrate at the same time various soil horizons and soil properties.
Finally a subdivision of various soil units is made in soil phases. It is a sub-

division in view of soil management. The main soil phases are as follows.

Stony phase   For soils with many stones, boulders or rock outcrops, that hinder the use of agricultural machines.
Lithic phase   For soils less than 50 cm deep on hard rock.
Petric phase   For soils with a volume fraction of ironstone concretions more than 40% or with a layer of coarse fragments >25 cm thick in the upper 100 cm.
Petrocalcic phase   For soils with a continuous indurated calcic horizon in the upper 100 cm.
Petrogypsic phase   For soils with a continuous indurated gypsic horizon in the upper 100 cm.
Petroferric phase   For soils with a continuous layer of ironstone in the upper 100 cm. See Plate 13.
Fragipan phase   For soils with a fragipan in the upper 100 cm. Such a pan is a very slowly permeable clay layer that is hard when dry and slakes or fractures if placed in water.
Duripan phase   For soils with a cemented layer of silica in the upper 100 cm.
Saline phase   For soils with highly soluble salts ($>4 \, EC_e$) in the upper 100 cm but not a Solonchak.
Sodic phase   For soils with an exchangeable sodium percentage (ESP) of more than 6%.

The indication of such soil phases is crucial when studying soils for agricultural purposes. In more detailed surveys on a national or regional level or in studies in land development projects, various other soil phases may be introduced, and those indicated above can be subdivided for example by the depth (maximum and minimum) of groundwater. All such soil properties are not included in the soil classification but are necessary for agricultural evaluation of soils. So they are mapped as soil phases. Rooting depth or rooting volume (extremely useful information) can also be shown as soil phases. Another relevant factor is hydraulic conductivity of soil layers to a depth of 4 or 5 m below the surface, if a drainage system has to be planned. Deep layers with a slow permeability for water highly influence drainage conditions of soils.

In practical investigations, the properties used to characterize the soil phases are usually so important that they are used first. For example, it is efficient to combine in one mapping unit all soils that are too shallow, too stony or rocky, or too steep. Areas that can be ignored are thus eliminated. Afterwards more time is available to study the useful soils.

Selected literature: Committee on Tropical Soils (1972); FAO (1970 a; 1973 a; 1973 c; 1977; 1971-1978); Kapagé (1976); Mohr et al. (1972); Proceedings (1977); Sanchez (1976); Soil Survey Staff (1951; 1975); Soil Science Soc. of America (1978); Vine (1968); Webster (1977); Young (1976).

3   The major soils of the world

3.1   Histosols

This is the most isolated group of major soils consisting of organic material. All following soils are mineral soils. Histosols have a histic H horizon. They are often called 'peat soils' and occur in wet low-lying areas. The layer of dead organic material has a thickness of at least 40 cm, mostly it is one or more metres thick. The organic material does not oxidize because it is under water. The composition of the organic matter is related to the original vegetation. The rate of decomposition varies. Lignins are often the main component. There are *Dystric Histosols* (pH < 5.5) and *Eutric Histosols* (pH $\geqslant$ 5.5).

In the tropics, large areas of Histosols occur in Malaysia and Indonesia (Sumatra and Kalimantan), mainly in coastal regions. Many mineral subsoils consist of sulphidic material, the parent material of poor acid sulphate soils, now called Thionic Fluvisols (Section 3.4). If such subsoils are shallow, reclamation is dangerous. Reclamation of Histosols can give various other problems, because the organic material will mineralize, and another consequence of drainage is subsidence of the surface soil. Moreover there is a shortage of plant nutrients, including minor elements like copper. Some Histosols are suitable for horticultural crops. In tropical mountain areas, Histosols may occur at flat high elevations over impermeable rocks.

Selected literature: Aandahl et al. (1972).

3.2   Lithosols

These soils are mineral soils less than 10 cm thick, over hard rock. They occur everywhere, particularly in mountainous regions. Often soil material has been eroded when the original vegetation (forests) was destroyed, and a very thin soil layer remains. These soils have no agricultural value. Some may be poor grazing land.

Most soils to be used for agricultural purposes should be at least 80 cm or more deep to have good rooting volume and sufficient water-holding capacity. Soils less than 50 cm deep over hard rock are a lithic phase of the particular major soils. In practice, more phases can be distinguished, e.g. for a soil depth of < 50 cm, 50-80 cm, 80-120 cm, 120-200 cm, 200-300 cm, > 300 cm.

3.3 Vertisols

These are heavy, often dark, clay soils (clay > 30%) in large flat areas that have a pronounced dry season during which they shrink and have large deep cracks (more than 1 cm wide at a depth of 50 cm) in a polygonal pattern (Figure 1). Other characteristics are a gilgai microrelief (Figure 2) or slickensides (Figure 3) at some depth. During the dry season, small soil aggregates of the surface layer fall in the cracks and partly fill them up. When rain starts, soils become wet and the clay swells. As cracks are filled up there is a pressure in the subsoil, which is partly pushed to the surface. This causes an irrigular microrelief called gilgai. The pressure in the subsoil also causes the formation of slickensides, polished and grooved soil aggregate surfaces. The material above the slickensides is mechanically mixed. The last process is called churning or pedoturbation. The dark upper soil horizon is therefore relatively deep. Some small lime concretions formed in the subsoil are pushed to the surface during this process. The surface layer to a depth of some centimetres often has a loose granular structure, also a result of alternating wetting and drying. This process is called self-mulching. Some Vertisols have hard dense surface layers and do not have self-mulching.

The clay in Vertisols is a montmorillonitic clay that swells and shrinks. It is formed when sufficient magnesium is present together with lime to maintain a high pH. The dark colour of the surface layer results from combination of some organic matter with clay particles. The content of organic matter in Vertisols is often no more than 0.5 or 1%. The soil has a high water retention, but relatively small amount of water is available for plant growth. Biological activity is limited. Vertisols are rather uniform over large areas. They are higly susceptible to water erosion.

Pellic Vertisols are dark, almost black, usually occupying shallow depressions that are somewhat waterlogged during the rainy season; *Chromic Vertisols* are brownish and better drained. Moreover there are many clay soils not having all specific characteristics of real Vertisols; they only have some characteristics such as cracks (not deep enough or not wide enough) or slickensides in the subsoils. Such soil are indicated as 'vertic'.

Vertisols occur over large areas in Australia, the Sudan, Chad and India, and in many other tropical and subtropical countries in regions with a pronounced dry season. Soils with vertic characteristics occur in almost all countries with such a climate.

Fig. 1. Deep and wide cracks in a Chromic Vertisol in the Sudan.

Fig. 2. Typical gilgai relief in a Chromic Vertisol in the Sudan.

Fig. 3. Slickenside in a Vertisol in Portugal.

Vertisols have fairly good, but limited agricultural potentialities, because the land is rather difficult to prepare. Dry soils are hard, and wet soils are very sticky. There is only a short period when moisture condition of the surface layer is favourable to prepare land for sowing and planting. Another difficulty is that drainability of the subsoil is very low, because of the swelling clay. Many areas with Vertisols are used for grazing. In the Sudan and in India, Vertisols are also used for growing cotton, hence the name 'Black cotton soil'. One of the oldest, large irrigation schemes, the Gezira Scheme in the Sudan, is on Vertisols. Generally precipitation during the rainy season is sufficient to prevent salinization of soils, but when precipitation is limited salinity problems might occur. Because of the low permeability and the low drainability of the subsoil, it is difficult to improve such soils. Originally soils in the Gezira Scheme were used for growing cotton only once in three years. Precipitation during two fallow years was enough to leach the small amounts of soluble salts brought into the area with irrigation water. Besides cotton, various other crops can be grown like wheat, lucerne, sugar-cane, groundnuts. Vertisol clay is unsuitable for brick making.

Selected references: Dudal (1965); Fink (1963).

3.4 Fluvisols

Fluvisols are young soils developed in recent alluvial deposits of river plains, deltas, former lakes (lacustrine deposits) and coastal areas (marine deposits). Soils consist to a great depth of various thin layers of sediment of differing texture. In the biologically influenced upper part of these soils, the sediment stratification has disappeared. Sediments consist of material eroded from uplands and mountains. Marine sediments have been transported by seawater. The mineralogical composition of the soil material is related to the types of rocks, their weathering products and alterations during soil formation before transport. Rivers originating in tropical regions transport mainly highly weathered material, whereas rivers with large catchment areas in temperate regions transport less intensively weathered sediments. Natural fertility of soils consisting of less weathered sediments is higher. Tropical marine sediments mostly have a very low lime content, whereas subtropical marine sediments may be calcareous.

Soil conditions in river plains, deltas and coastal areas are highly variable because of the type and pattern of sedimentation of the material. In valleys and deltas, river terraces and various types of basins (backswamps) occur. Coastal areas are characterized by beach walls, depressional and lagoonal areas. Lacustrine deposits are more uniform. Some soils in depressions may have a histic H horizon or may be Histosols. Some have an umbric A horizon, but most soils have an ochric A horizon. Older soils in arid and semi-arid regions as well as older rice soils (Paddy soils, Section 3.6) have a layer of irrigation sediments. In older irrigated plains and deltas, such an irrigation deposit may be some metres thick. In arid regions, many soils are saline and belong to Solonchaks (Section 3.5), or if salinity is less to the saline phase of Fluvisols.

Fluvisols with calcareous material are called *Calcaric Fluvisols,* those in non-calcareous material *Eutric Fluvisols,* except when the base saturation is below 50%, which are *Dystric Fluvisols* (Plate 1). In coastal areas, *Thionic Fluvisols* (formerly called cat-clay soils or acid sulphate soils) occur in the zone of brackish water, when lime content of the soil material is low and there is organic matter. The Thionic Fluvisols have sulphid material at a depth of less than 125 cm. Sulphur originates from sea-water. In a biochemical process, pyrite (FeS_2) is formed in the presence of organic matter (Mangrove and Avicennia), and in the absence of lime. The reduced soil has a blackish tinge. If such a soil is drained and oxidation starts, $FeSO_4$ and H_2SO_4 are formed, and finally jarosite. yellowish basic ferrisulphate ($Fe(OH)SO_4$) spots, which characterize the soils. The soil pH decreases on oxidation to 3 or 2 and hardly any plant can grow, as aluminium becomes soluble and is highly toxic. The Thionic Fluvisols are very poor soils, particularly once they are aerated. They can be improved by adding lime, but large amounts are needed. Before reclaiming coastal areas, particularly in the tropics, presence or absence of sulphid material has to be investigated. A simple test is oxidation with hydroperoxide and measurement of pH.

The other Fluvisols are generally good agricultural soils and often intensively used, although land use has to be adapted to floods, inundations and high groundwater. Soils with a deeper groundwater level (levees and beach walls) are suitable for a wide range of crops. Soils of basins are often used for growing rice. They may have the properties of Paddy soils, a man-made soil (Section 3.6). Unirrigated Fluvisols can be subdivided according to drainage conditions (depth of groundwater and less permeable layers), soil texture and rooting depth (often the depth to the stratified subsoil).

In low-lying areas in coastal regions, deltas and former lakes, sediments can be deposited in permanent submerged conditions. Consequently the packing of the clay particles is very loose (mud-clays). Upon drainage, a specific type of initial soil formation takes place. This has physical, biological and chemical aspects, because the permanently reduced mud is changing into a normal oxidized soil; it has to 'ripen', and the process is called 'ripening'. The mud-clay loses water and dries out, the mud shrinks irreversibly and there is a gradual subsidence of the surface as ripening extends to deeper layers. Oxidation and decarbonation are the main chemical processes. Biological activity starts with root penetration and formation of organic matter. During soil ripening, the loose water-saturated mud-clay is transformed into a normal soil and various stages of development can be recognized that are relevant during reclamation. Presence of sulphid and mud-clay subsoils often remain unrecognized. This is a main reason why various development projects in Fluvisols have failed.

Selected literature: Pons and Zonneveld (1965); Proceedings (1973).

3.5 Solonchaks

Solonchaks are highly saline soils containing soluble salts that influence plant growth. They are poor soils because most plants cannot grow at all. Some soils can be improved by drainage and washing out of salts with additional irrigation water (Plate 2). These soils occur in arid and semi-arid regions and in regions with shallow, highly saline, groundwater. Irrigated land in dry regions can easily become saline, even if irrigation water is of a good quality, because all irrigation water contains some soluble salts. During each irrigation a small amount of salt remains in the soil, that finally becomes saline after 20 or 30 years. Even if natural drainage of such soils is good and groundwater is deep, such soils become saline. As a consequence of irrigation the groundwater rises towards the surface, often with a speed of one metre per year. After some years or decades the saline groundwater has reached the rooting zone of crops.

The harmful soluble salts are chlorides ($NaCl$, $CaCl_2$, $MgCl_2$), sulphates (Na_2SO_4, $MgSO_4$), nitrates ($NaNO_3$, KNO_3), carbonates (Na_2CO_3), bicarbonates ($NaHCO_3$) and borates. Most common are the chlorides and sulphates. The carbonates and bicarbonates are discussed in Section 3.15 Solonetz. Salinization caused by nitrates and borates are exceptions. The highly soluble chlorides and sulphates originate from sedimentary rocks of uplifted former lagoons, from sea-water or from aeolian dusts or cyclic salts. Highly soluble salts present in soils increase the osmotic pressure of the soil moisture, affecting the plant's ability to take up water from the soil and resulting in physiological drought, a characteristic phenomenon of crops on saline land.

Moreover the ion-balance in the soil water is disturbed and crops show signs of nutrient deficiencies. Crops develop poorly and irregularly because salts are irregularly distributed in the field. This is caused by slight differences in soil permeability and in microrelief.

Salts in soils occur as crystals, as a solution in soil water or in groundwater. The salt concentration changes continually because of evapotranspiration, evaporation, and irrigation. In soils influenced by sea-water, NaCl is the main salt. Other soils contain mixtures of various salts; sometimes chlorides, sometimes sulphates predominate. The solubility of the various salts is different and depends not only on soil temperature but also on the kinds and amounts of salts. The theory of the various salinization processes is complicated.

For practical purposes, most important is to know the amount of highly soluble salts present in soils. This can be determined chemically or electrically. Chemically total soluble salts (TSS) are determined and expressed as a mass fraction (%) or in parts per million (ppm) or various salts are analysed and expressed as a concentration of ionic equivalent (meq/1). Mostly, however, the electrical resistance (in ohms) in an extract of a water-saturated soil sample is measured on a Wheatstone-bridge at 25 °C with two electrodes of one square centimetre and one centimetre apart. The reciprocal value of the electrical resistance is called electrical conductivity and expressed in $EC_e.10^3$ (milli mho's). If salt concentrations are low, e.g. in irrigation water, salt content is expressed in micro-mhos. The letter e in EC_e refers to a measurement in a water extract. If measurements are made in a soil paste the letter p is used, for example EC_p. The paste procedure is less accurate. Generally the following interpretation of the soil salinity status is accepted:

salinity class	$EC_e.10^3$	TSS (%)
salt-free	0- 2	0 -0.15
slightly saline	2- 8	0.15-0.35
moderately saline	8-15	0.35-0.65
strongly saline	>15	>0.65

This classification is rather rough, for instance because it indicates the salinity status of soils when they are saturated, it does not take account of composition of salts, soil temperature in the field is not exactly 25 °C, and various crops have different tolerance to various types of salts. All the same this analysis is made all over the world, applied to all saline soils, and is sufficient for practical purposes. On the FAO/Unesco Soil Map of the World, Solonchaks have more than 15 $EC_e.10^3$ of soluble salt somewhere in the soil within a depth of 125 cm for sandy soils and within the upper 75 cm for clay soils, or 4 $EC_e.10^3$ in the 25 cm surface layer if the pH exceeds 8.5. This means that only highly saline soils are indicated as Solonchaks. Soils with a lower content of soluble salts have been mapped as 'saline phase'.

Besides the irregular growth of corps and the characteristics of drought saline soils can also be recognized by a halophytic vegetation, or by salt crystals on the soil surface or on a profile wall a few days old. A simple test is to taste a small amount of soil material. A salty taste indicates strong salinity; a slightly bitter taste also indicates the presence of sodium sulphate. Soils rich in Na_2SO_4 have a puffy or fluffy surface layer, because the rather long salt needles separate soil particles. Soils with much $MgCl_2$ or $CaCl_2$ have the colour of the moist soil, because these chlorides are hygroscopic and attract moisture from the air, particularly during the night. They are called 'Sabakh soils' in the Middle East. Some extremely saline soils have a white salt crust at the surface.

For saline soils, samples of the surface soil have to be taken from various spots that are characterised by salt efflorescences, differences in crop growth or microrelief. In a soil profile, samples have to be taken at regular intervals, because salt content is not related to soil horizons. Groundwater has to be sampled for analysis together with samples of a profile.

Most Solonchaks are *Orthic Solonchaks* (Plate 2), the normal Solonchaks. If they have hydromorphic properties caused by shallow groundwater within the upper 50 cm, they are called *Gleyic Solonchaks*. In semi-arid regions, saline soils may have a mollic A horizon and are called *Mollic Solonchaks*. Some others are called *Takyric Solonchaks,* because they have a heavy clay texture with polygonal cracks and a platy massive surface and occur in a rather barren landscape, as in the southern part of the Soviet Union.

From the description of Solonchaks, one learns that only highly saline soils are indicated as such. There are, however, many soils with less soluble salts, but still enough to retard crop growth and to give low yields. Such soils and particularly those that have soluble salts only in a deeper layer are dangerous, because salinity often goes unrecognized. However as soon as irrigation starts, salinity increases rapidly.

The agricultural evaluation of Solonchaks has already been given. In saline soils, even real Solonchaks, that have a moderate to rapid permeability to a depth of at least 3 m, and that can be drained, the harmful soluble salts can be washed out, and carried away in drainwater. When this is completed, soils may have high agricultural potential, although it is necessary to apply fertilizers and to take care that salts cannot accumulate in the rooting zone again. The success of many reclamation projects on salt-affected soils is low, because drainage is not sufficient (groundwater table is still too high; the distance between field drains is too large), the maintenance of the system is poor, or the areas of poor soils or of soils that are difficult to improve and that are included in a project is too large. Many farmers who have the experience of some generations know how in specific conditions some crops can still be grown. Some crops tolerate a somewhat higher salinity than others. Some tolerant crops are date palms, barley, cotton, sugar-beet, although none of them can grow well on real Solonchaks. Among very sensitive crops are most fruit crops, green beans, and field beans.

Selected literature: Richards (1954); FAO/Unesco (1973).

3.6 Gleysols

There are many poorly drained soils, often in low-lying areas and in depressions, that are influenced by high groundwater and therefore show hydromorphic properties. Such soils are Gleysols if these phenomena occur within a depht of less than 50 cm of the surface (Plate 3). Soils with hydromorphic properties and consisting of recent alluvial deposits are excluded; they are Fluvisols (Section 3.4). Solonchaks with high groundwater are excluded as well (Section 3.5). If only the lower part of other soils are influenced by groundwater, they are considered to be 'gleyic' (e.g. Gleyic Luvisols). Because of the high ground water, Gleysols have a reducing condition in the part of the soil that is continuously saturated with water. There is no free or dissolved oxygen and the soil is therefore grayish-blue. In the zone of a fluctuating ground water, grayish-blue spots and orange or reddish spots (segregation of iron) or small blackish spots (segregation of manganese) are found, whereas in the upper part of some Gleysols, that is not within the reach of groundwater, the soil is permanently oxidized and the reduction and oxidation spots do not occur. Presence of a histic H horizon also indicates hydromorphic conditions. Some soils have hydromorphic properties due to stagnating water on a less permeable subsoil layer (pseudogley).

Many Gleysols in the tropics are used for growing wet rice. During the rainy season they are inundated, or they have a controlled irrigation system. When such soils are almost exclusively used for growing rice a typical kind of Gleysol is formed, called Paddy soil, discussed below. For crops that do not like reducing conditions in the rooting zone, Gleysols may be improved by drainage. The groundwater table is lowered. This is done mainly in a drainage project in which open or closed fielddrains carry excess water to a drainage ditch that brings the water to a drainage canal, and finally a pumping station ensures a low water level in the canals. Small areas can sometimes be drained by a simple windpump.

Soil fertility of Gleysols depends on the type of parent material and on the depth of groundwater, that sets a limit to the rooting system.

Gleysols in the tropics may have plinthite (Section 4.5) within 125 cm of the surface and are called *Plinthic Gleysols*. Those with a mollic A or umbric A horizon are respectively called *Mollic Gleysols* and *Humic Gleysols*. If soil material is calcareous, they are *Calcaric Gleysols*, and those with base saturations of less than 50% or more than 50% are respectively called *Dystric Gleysols* and *Eutric Gleysols* (Plate 3).

In the tropics, Plinthic Gleysols and Dystric Gleysols are rather common. In the subtropics, the other Gleysols are more common, although they may occur at greater altitude in the tropics.

Paddy soils

There is one group of soils with typical hydromorphic characteristics that has to be mentioned here, although these soils are not on the Soil Map of the World and not specially classified in various systems of soil classification. These are the flooded rice soils, Sawah soils, Paddy soils or Paddi soils, a type of 'man-made soil' (also called Anthropogenic soils), because soil conditions are highly influenced by human activity. An example is given in Plate 16. These soils cover an area of about 100 million hectares. They occur mainly in river-plains, deltas and low coastal plains of South East Asia. In the tropics are also many wet rice fields on flat and sloping land, where the original soils were Acrisols, Ferralsols, Vertisols or Andosols. There are intricate irrigation systems to flood the paddy fields that occupy terraces on slopes. These terraces are man-made; terrace walls are built and much soil material has been transported to get level fields, that often are very small. Here too, typical Paddy soils have been formed, because the upper part of these soils is in a reduced and the lower part in an oxidized condition. Therefore there are two rather different types of Paddy soils, the flooded soils with a completely reduced subsoil, and those formed in originally well drained soils still having an oxidized subsoil.

In all Paddy soils, a thin plough-layer or plough-sole is formed. This is a dense poorly permeable layer at the depth of cultivation, formed as a result of ploughing or puddling of the surface soil in flooded conditions. Water percolation in this dense layer is very slow. In the flooded rice fields in alluvial plains with a permanently high groundwater table, the whole soil is to some degree, reduced because of anaerobic conditions. There may be some rust spots. Only the uppermost centimetre of soil may be somewhat oxidized by some oxygen in the water layer above. In Paddy soils without a permanently high groundwater table, the surface layer under the layer of irrigation water is similar. Below the plough-layer, soils are oxidized. There is a horizon with mainly iron (reddish-brown) and somewhat lower a horizon with mainly manganese (black spots) accumulation. As a result of an intensive reduction process in the surface layer, caused by anaerobic conditions, iron and manganese are partly mobile and precipitate in the oxidized subsoil.

If such Paddy soils are used for growing unirrigated crops (in a dry season), the surface soil becomes oxidized, but the plough-layer limits root development. Blue-green algae in Paddy soils fix rather large amounts of nitrogen; therefore continuous rice cropping is possible. Yields can often be considerably increased by adding ammonium fertilizers. Paddy soils of terraced volcano slopes profit from fertile irrigation water. Crop yields of paddy generally depend more on proper irrigation (control of the amount of irrigation water and time of application) than on soil conditions.

Selected literature: Mohr et al. (1972); Kawaguchi and Kyuma (1977); Young (1976); Moormann and van Breemen (1978).

3.7 Andosols

Andosols occur in volcanic regions, often on mountain slopes. They are formed in volcanic ash material, and have a dark mollic or umbric A horizon often over a cambic B horizon. See Plate 4. The ash material is very light, its bulk density being less than 0.85 g.cm⁻³ (850 kg.m⁻³). Much material is amorphous, not well crystallized, giving the soil a smeary consistence (soils are thixotropic). The clay is characterized by dominance of allophane (amorphic hydrated aluminium silicates of various composition). Rather recent volcanic ash soils that have ≥60% vitric volcanic ash are called *Vitric Andosols*; they also occur in rather arid regions. Andosols with a mollic A horizon are *Mollic Andosols*; those with an umbric A horizon are *Humic Andosols*, which often occur in cool and humid regions, in the tropics at altitudes of some hundred metres or more (Plate 4). If there is only an ochric A and a cambic B horizon and soils have a smeary consistence, they are *Ochric Andosols*. Most Andosols are good for agriculture, often the best soils in the tropics, particularly if they are formed in intermediate or basic volcanic material. Andosols can absorb much water, the CEC is high (35-54 mmol per 100 g) and they contain much organic matter (5-20%). Natural fertility is high. Most Andosols are very porous. Irrigated rice fields on Andosols have less permeable layers of iron and of manganese accumulation (Paddy soils, Section 3.6).

On maturing in the humid tropics, allophane is transformed into metahalloysite and finally into kaolinite, and consequently in older volcanic regions there are various transitional soils to Ferralsols. In Vitric and sometimes in Ochric Andosols of andesitic origin in the humid tropics, a silica-cemented hard pan (duripan) is formed. It is hard when dry, and fragile when moist. It is slightly permeable to water and almost impermeable to roots.

In a broad zone around young volcanos, many soils have received some volcanic ash. The original soils would be, for instance, Ferralsols, Nitosols or Acrisols. They are rejuvenated and may now have much better chemical properties than originally.

3.8 Arenosols

These are very light-coloured (light gray, very pale or white) coarse-textured sandy soils with a high proportion of almost pure quartz (Plate 5). If it is albic material, it should be at least 50 cm thick. The subsoil may show characteristics of an argillic, cambic or oxic B horizon. They do not, however, have such horizons because the soil texture is too coarse.

Usually these soils do not belong to one of the major soils characterized by an argillic, a cambic or an oxic B horizon, because they are too light-textured. Arenosols have a lower water retention, are more permeable, have a lower natural fertility and a lower CEC than other soils. Deficiencies of various minor elements are common. They may have an ochric A horizon..

If Arenosols consist of albic material they are called *Albic Arenosols.* Those with thin layers of clay accumulation are *Luvic Arenosols,* a coarse-textured variant of the real Luvisols (Section 3.25). Arenosols with characteristics of Ferralsols (Section 3.13) have ferralic properties and are called *Ferralic Arenosols* (Plate 5), and finally there are *Cambic Arenosols,* which have a cambic-like but too light-textured horizon.

Arenosols are poor for agriculture. Natural vegetation is often forest. As soon as trees are cut, soils may erode and land becomes rather poor grazing land. Natural fertility is low.

3.9 Regosols

Regosols are very young soils, almost without soil development. There is only an ochric A horizon. All other diagnostic horizons are absent. They consist mostly of loose soil material without or with very weak soil development, for example young dunes. Regosols retain little water. Some dunes are used for coconut cultivation.

3.10 Rankers

Soils with only an umbric A horizon of less than 25 cm are called Rankers.The A horizon is mostly direct on hard rock consisting of siliceous material. They have hardly any agricultural value, because rooting depth is limited, and there are many stones and rock outcrops.

3.11 Rendzinas

These soils have only a mollic A horizon over calcareous rock material. Similar to Rankers, they have hardly any agricultural value. (In older literature, the name 'Rendzina' has been used for quite different soils).

3.12 Podzols

Podzols are well known in the northern hemisphere. They are characterized by a spodic B horizon, which is a horizon in the subsoil cemented by organic matter with iron or aluminium or both (humus-iron pan, as in Plate 6). In the tropics, podzols occur in very siliceous sands, without weatherable minerals, for example in some very poor coastal sanddunes or in poor inland sands. Humus and iron components are leached and carried off to ground water, rivers and low-lying areas, or accumulate in subsoils, sometimes at a depth of some metres. The sandy material of the upper part of the soil consists of bleached white-gray quartz grains. Vegetation is poor. Soils have a very low agricultural value. Soils with a very thick surface layer of bleached sand (white sands) are Albic Arenosols (Section 3.8). Podzols are poor forest and grazing soils. Their extent is very limited in the tropics; *Gleyic Podzols* (with hydromorphic properties in the upper 50 cm) and *Humic Podzols* (with dispersed organic matter in the B horizon) occur there (Plate 6).

3.13 Ferralsols

These are real tropical soils, with an oxic B horizon (Plate 7). Such a horizon is at least 30 cm thick, has $> 15\%$ clay, diffuse horizon boundaries, no weatherable minerals and a CEC of clay < 16 me per 100 g. Ferralsols are in general the real reddish or yellowish very uniform tropical clay soils with an ochric A horizon and a deep B horizon, otherwise almost characterless. The soil profile looks uniform and may be some metres thick. It is well drained, has a good permeability and a stable structure. As there is little or no weatherable mineral, because these soils are old and exhausted of bases, natural fertility is very low. The normal Ferralsols are called *Orthic Ferralsols* (Plate 7) but there are five other groups of Ferralsols. Many have ground water influence and consequently plinthite is formed (Section 4.4). If this occurs within the zone 0-125 cm, they are *Plinthic Ferralsols*. Plinthite is an iron-rich clay material visible as pronounced red mottles; it is firm and can be cut with a spade or knife in a moist soil. When it is exposed, it dries out, becomes hard and changes irreversibly to ironstone. This may form a real ironstone hardpan or hard ironstone concretions. As long as it is moist and not hardened it is called plinthite. When it is hardened, it is ironstone (old names: laterite, laterite concretions). Most Ferralsols in the humid tropics are found at low altitudes. At somewhat higher altitudes, temperature is somewhat lower, mineralization of organic matter is lower and some Ferralsols may have an umbric horizon or a higher content of organic matter in the B horizon, being *Humic Ferralsols*. Real old Ferralsols have a very low CEC of the clay fraction ($\leqslant 1.5$ me per 100 g), they are the *Acric Ferralsols*. Some have a very red to dusky red B horizon and are called *Rhodic Ferralsols*, whereas those with a yellowish or pale yellow B horizon, because of a low iron content, are the *Xanthic Ferralsols*.

These clayey soils weathered to a great depth without distinct horizons and with uniform profiles with good physical and poor chemical characteristics are characterized by kaolinitic clay minerals with low CEC, and often by low V. There has been a complicated process of soil formation. Intensive and continuous weathering over a very long period has resulted in leaching of bases and silica, in relative accumulation of sesquioxides (iron and aluminium oxides) and in formation of kaolinitic clays (1:1 lattice clays). Soils are continuously moist (humid tropics), and there is an almost continuous percolation of water in a porous soil. Clay particles are often cemented by iron, and therefore the content of water-dispersible clay is low. Silt content is often low too. Available water for plant growth is less than expected from soil texture. Biological activity in these soils is high, particularly under forest, and there is an extensive root system. A real virgin tropical forest produces five times as much organic matter than a forest in a temperate climate. In the humid tropics, decomposition of organic matter is also five times as great. There are many soil organisms; termites are particularly active in many soils.

Although Ferralsols may be considered as typical soils of the humid tropics, they do not occupy such large areas. Many have plinthite or ironstone layers, or they have a stone line (a thin layer of quartz or ironstone gravels at some depth). Some of them show clearly that the soil material has been deposited where it is now, after erosion somewhere in the neighbourhood, as can be observed also from differences in clay, silt and sand content of various layers of a Ferralsol. There have often been changes in climate during old geological periods that have influenced soil formation in various regions, so Ferralsols may also be found outside the humid tropics.

Lighter-textured soils with ferralic soil properties are Ferralic Arenosols (Section 3.8; Plate 5); those that still have some weatherable material but have a cambic horizon, not a real oxic B horizon, are called *Ferralic Cambisols* (Section 3.26).

The process of soil formation by which Ferralsols are formed is called ferralitization. One of the characteristics is the leaching of silica as mentioned above. This silica may seep with groundwater to valleys and other low areas where it can produce smectoid clays (2:1 lattice clays) like montmorillionite, the typical clay mineral of Vertisols; however not all Vertisols are formed in this way.

For agriculture, Ferralsols are important, but chemically very poor, not only because of a low CEC but also because of deficiency of bases like Ca, Mg and K, strong P fixation, and high exchangeable Al percentage. So they need fertilizers, often also lime and some other elements like S and Zn. Ferralsols with some organic matter react better to fertilizers than Ferralsols with little organic matter. Fertilizer trials are needed in association with soil sample analysis or foliar analysis. Presence of plinthite and the danger of hardening limits agricultural potential. Cultivation of these and similar tropical soils results in a gradual decrease in organic matter. Organic matter in these soils is extremely important, because the CEC of the kaolinitic clays is very low. Ferralsols with a higher base saturation are better than those with a lower one, which often have a high Al saturation, causing Al toxicity, overcome by liming such soils. If possible, lime should be mixed with the soil, because Al toxicity limits the rooting depth of crops. Rhodic Ferralsols, having a somewhat better nutrient status, are considered the best Ferralsols. They response better to fertilizers and are often used for plantation crops.

Until recently, there has been much confusion in classifying and naming tropical soils, particularly what are now Ferralsols in the FAO scheme, and Oxisols in Soil Taxonomy (Chapter 6). Older names of various classification systems are: Lateritic soils, Latosols, Ferrallitic soils, Kaolisols.

Selected literature: Wambeke (1974); various publications of ORSTOM in French.

3.14 Planosols

These are soils with seasonal waterlogging and strong leaching with an albic E horizon over a clay pan. Such a clay pan is a slowly permeable horizon (argillic or natric B horizon with an abrupt textural change), or a heavy clay layer. Consequently there is in the wet season stagnating water in the E horizon, which therefore shows hydromorphic properties due to alternating reduction and oxidation. When the atmost impermeable clay layer has an ESP (exchangeable sodium percentage; see Section 3.15) of more than 6, it is called a *Solodic Planosol* (Plate 8), a new name for the former Solods, a degraded Solonetz, that generally does not occur over large areas.

Planosols with a mollic A horizon or with an umbric A horizon are respectively called *Mollic Planosols* and *Humic Planosols*. Most Planosols in the tropics are those having an ochric A horizon and a base saturation (V) of less than 50%: *Dystric Planosols*. Some may have a V $>50\%$: *Eutric Planosols*. They are formed in flat areas or in shallow depressions and have very poor drainage. During the rainy season, the upper part of the soil is waterlogged, and therefore they are often used for growing rice. Although these soils are agriculturally poor, they may be good for rice and some other crops. Agricultural potentiality is rather low.

3.15 Solonetz

Solonetz are characterized by a natric B horizon, being a soil horizon some decimetres below the soil surface in which fine clay particles that are leached from the surface layer accumulate. It is a kind of argillic B horizon (Section 4.3) that also has a high (>15) sodium percentage at the adsorption complex. This is caused by the presence of salts like $NaHCO_3$ or Na_2CO_3, which are highly soluble and sodium ions are exchanged with calcium ions on the ion-exchange complex. Therefore clay particles and humus are easily eluviated from the A horizon into the B horizon that has a prismatic structure with clay and humus coatings on the ped surfaces. The latter give the horizon a dark colour. The presence of sodium carbonate and bicarbonate increases the pH of the soil beyond 8.5, often to 9 or 10. This can also be observed in the ground water that turns red if some drops of phenol pH indicator are added. Some of these drops on the soil turn it purple.

Solonetz are often found in arid and semi-arid areas, as are Solonchaks (Section 3.5). In arid regions, the natric B horizon occurs at a shallow depth. As a consequence of the high percentage of Na on the complex, soil structure deteriorates. A high content of magnesium on the soil complex may have a similar effect to sodium; therefore it is determined that, if the ionic equivalent of exchangeable Mg^{2+} and Na^+ is more than the sum of exchangeable Ca^{2+} and H^+, this also may characterize a natric B horizon. The percentage sodium (Na^+) is expressed as exchangeable sodium percentage (ESP) of the cation-exchange complex (CEC). If the ESP is less than 5, it is not very harmful; if it is more than 15, soils have or develop poor physical conditions.

In a soil extract, as made to determine the salt content of a soil (Section 3.5), the sodium adsorption ratio (SAR) can be used to indicate soil sodicity. The formula: $SAR = Na^+ \times [0.5 (Ca^{2+} + Mg^{2+})]^{-0.5}$ is used, where cations refer to concentrations in meq.1^{-1}. A SAR of 12 is almost equivalent to an ESP of 15.

The processes related to the presence of sodium carbonate and bicarbonate are called sodication, a word replacing the word 'alkalization' used until recently. The name Alkali soil also has been abandoned.

Besides the real Solonetz, there are many soils not having a completely natric B horizon or having an ESP somewhat less than 15%. They can be referred to as a sodic phase. Most Solonetz in somewhat humid regions are *Orthic Solonetz*. In continental semi-arid regions, *Mollic Solonetz* with a mollic A horizon occur. The last ones are often found in association with Phaeozems and Kastanozems (Section 3.19 and 3.18). *Gleyic Solonetz* show hydromorphic properties in the upper 50 cm.

For agriculture Solonetz have poor physical conditions because of the natric B horizon and the deteriorated soil structure. They can be improved by applying gypsum. Then the Na^+ on the adsorbing complex is replaced by Ca^{2+} of the gypsum. Sometimes Solonetz are improved by deep-ploughing and applying gypsum. The upper metre or more of the soil is completely mixed.

Saline soils often also may have a high ESP or SAR; when such soils are reclaimed, a dressing of gypsum is required. Solonchaks situated near gypsiferous desert areas like the Mesopotamian Plain get enough gypsum during dust storms to avoid sodification. Lands reclaimed from the sea or immersed in saline water easily sodify if they are not calcareous, particularly during the last stage of leaching of salts and consequently an application of gypsum is needed.

There are also soils that have a natric B horizon with a columnar or prismatic structure and tongues of the eluvial horizon with uncoated silt or sand grains extending into the B horizon, that were formerly called Solodized Solonetz and that are now included in Solonetz. Such soils form a transitional phase to the Solods, that are now included in the Solodic Planosols (Section 3.14).

Selected literature: FAO/Unesco (1973).

3.16 Greyzems

Soils with a dark mollic A horizon and bleached coatings on ped surfaces.

Many show clay illuvation and have an argillic B horizon. Some occur in the semi-arid subtropics.

3.17 Chernozems

Typical steppe soils of semi-arid continental regions (cold winters) with an almost black mollic A horizon and a calcic or gypsic horizon or concentration of powdery lime at shallow depth. There are *Luvic Chernozems* (with an argillic B horizon), *Glossic Chernozems* (with tonguing A horizon into the B horizon), *Calcic Chernozems* (with a calcic or gypsic horizon) and *Haplic Chernozems,* the common ones with enrichment of powdery lime. Chernozems are uncommon in tropical regions and do occur in the subtropics.

3.18 Kastanozems

These are soils similar to Chernozems; however the mollic A horizon is brown or dark brown. There are *Luvic, Calcic and Haplic Kastanozems,* with diagnostic properties similar to those described for Chernozems. Kastanozems may occur in continental semi-arid subtropical regions and also at high altitudes in the tropics and subtropics if climatic and biotic conditions are favourable (cool winters, a long dry season and grass vegetation).

3.19 Phaeozems

Mainly subtropical soils of prairie regions, characterized by a mollic A horizon and leaching of carbonates to a great depth. Unlike Chernozems, they have no calcic or gypsic horizon. *Luvic Phaeozems* have an argillic B horizon, *Calcaric Phaeozems* are calcareous, and *Haplic Phaeozems* are non-calcareous. These soils occur in tropical highlands. They are generally fertile and suitable for crops and grassland. In the subtropics, Luvic Phaeozems are better than Haplic Phaeozems because of a somewhat better water-holding capacity, as rainfall in the growing season is rather low.

3.20 Podzoluvisols

Soils with a bleached E horizon, deep tonguing into an argillic B horizon. *Dystric Podzoluvisols* have a base saturation of less than 50%; *Eutric Podzoluvisols* of more than 50%. They are not important in the tropics and seldom occur in the subtropics.

3.21 Xerosols

Xerosols are soils in arid and semi-arid regions with an aridic soil moisture regime, and a weakly developed ochric A horizon (Plate 9). Precipitation is low, mostly less than 100 or 200 mm per year, and the rainy period is rather short. Rain is not enough to grow crops; and land is rather poor grazing with short annual grasses. During the rainy season only the upper part of the soils becomes somewhat moist. The subsoils are always dry. Often the parent material is calcareous and some lime accumulates at a depth to which soils may become moist. Mostly there are some fine lime mycelia in the subsoil. These Xerosols are called *Haplic Xerosols*. When there is so much lime accumulation that a calcic horizon is formed, they are *Calcic Xerosols* (Plate 9), and when there is a gypsic horizon, *Gypsic Xerosols*. Finally there are Xerosols with an argillic B horizon, mostly at shallow depth, *Luvic Xerosols*. These are often rather old soils or soils in a transitional zone to Luvisols.

Xerosols are exposed to strong solar radiation. There is often much wind. Dust storms are common and the upper soil layers often blow away and accumulate somewhere else. The calcic or gypsic horizon may harden, forming a petrocalcic or a petrogypsic horizon, which is often also found at or near the surface, when the overlying soil material is blown off. If such cemented horizons are present in the upper 100 cm, such soils are mapped as petrocalcic or petrogypsic phases. Rain, although scarce, many come down in heavy showers of short duration and consequently the soil surface, which is often somewhat crusted, cannot take up all water. For a short period, large areas are submerged and the upper soil is transported to depression and drainage ways. In fact, the water absorped by the soil is therefore less than what is supplied by rain, except in depressions and on foodslopes, where more water can penetrate. There grass vegetation is more luxurious. An irregular topography is an advantage, because it decreases risk. Even in dry years, there is some grass in depressions and on foot slopes. Many grasses have an extensive root system, because all plants try to pick up as much water as possible.

Redistribution of carbonates and gypsum is the main soil-forming process. Powdery gypsum and particularly powdery lime and lime mycelia occur in many soils, except when the parent material does not have these components. In older clayey soils, an argillic B horizon can be formed as a result of sudden wetting of a completely dry soil, causing an appreciable rise in pH, and mobilization of some clay for a few hours only. It takes many centuries before a real argillic B horizon forms.

If a soil contains some gravel, as in old river terraces, and the fine soil material blows away, a gravel layer forms at the surface, called a desert pavement. Stony soils often have a real stony layer at the surface. Other soils may have a thin, dense and brittle surface seal or surface crust.

The agricultural value of Xerosols is low except when they can be irrigated and when physical properties are good for irrigated crops. However, most Xerosols cannot be irrigated because of absence of irrigation water. Many Xerosols are overgrazed, causing severe wind erosion.

As soon as precipitation increases and soils become moist to a depth of at least 80 cm, dry farming can be practised without too much risk. Most soils then form a cambic B horizon and are Cambisols (Section 3.26). A real problem in all semi-arid and arid regions is that precipitation is highly irregular from year to year, between seasons of the year, and also from place to place. The effective rainfall in the tropics is always much less than the total rainfall because of high evaporation. Most Xerosols are used for extensive sheep grazing; some can be irrigated.

Selected literature: Dregne (1976); UN Conference, Nairobi (1977).

3.22 Yermosols

The moisture regime of these soils is also aridic and they have a very weakly developed ochric A horizon, much less developed than in Xerosols. The content of organic matter is generally less than 0.5% in the upper 40 centimetres. Yermosols occur in real desert regions. They are even drier than Xerosols and there are similar groups, *Luvic Yermosols, Gypsic Yermosols* and *Haplic Yermosols,* for which reference is made to Section 3.21. In addition, there is a special group of *Takyric Yermosols* indicating that these soils have takyric features, in other words a heavy clay texture with a platy surface crust and cracks in a polygonal pattern. Such soils are found in flat areas of heavy clays in arid regions. They are not Vertisols (Section 3.3).

Some Yermosols consist of highly gypsiferous parent material. Although gypsum ($CaSO_4 . 2H_2O$) is not a highly soluble salt, such soils are not suitable for agriculture in irrigation projects, at least when the soil material of the root zone contains more than 10% gypsum. Even when the gypsum content of the upper soil layers is more than 5%, crop yields will be rather low. In gypsiferous subsoils with >25% gypsum, roots will not penetrate. Moreover highly gypsiferous soils cause serious problems when irrigated, because of solubility of the gypsiferous material. Most Yermosols can be used only for very extensive sheep grazing.

Selected literature: van Alphen and de los Rios (1971); Dregne (1976); UN Conference, Nairobi (1977).

3.23 Nitosols

Nitosols are clayey, red tropical soils with an argillic B horizon (low CEC) without abrupt textural changes and with a gradual decrease in clay content to a greater depth (less than 20% decrease in clay from its maximum to a depth of 150 cm). Nitosols do not have plinthite in the zone 0-125 cm, and do not have ferric or vertic properties. They occur in many tropical countries and have good potentialities for agriculture, because the deep, uniform profiles that are porous and well drained, have a stable angular to subangular blocky structure and consequently a deep rooting volume. Moreover they have a high moisture storage capacity, rather rich basic parent material, and some weatherable minerals. The clay is mainly kaolinitic. Nitosols have shiny ped surfaces to a great depth. This is a typical characteristic of Nitosols. The *Dystric Nitosols* (Plate 10) have a low base saturation (V $<50\%$), and the *Eutric Nitosols* have a high base saturation (V $>50\%$). Some Nitosols in regions with a somewhat cooler climate and V $<50\%$ may have an umbric A horizon and are called *Humic Nitosols*.

Nitosols are good for a wide range of crops. Nitosols with a high base saturation are better than those with a low one. The CEC is rather low; P fixation is common. The dry season is generally less than four months. Most Nitosols are somewhat susceptible to soil erosion.

In comparison with the Acrisols and Luvisols (described below, and also having an argillic B horizon), the difference in definition is clear. If there are plinthite, hydromorphic, ferric or vertic properties, the soils can never be Nitosols. The difference in the argillic horizon is: a much more abrupt textural change in the upper part of the more pronounced and distinct argillic B horizon in Acrisols and Luvisols. Moreover shiny ped surfaces do not occur in Acrisols and Luvisols. As there are many intergrades, it is sometimes difficult to differentiate beween related soils like Rhodic Ferralsols and Chromic Luvisols.

In most tropical countries, Nitosols are cultivated and extensively used to grow various crops. Natural fertility is relatively high but fertilizers are needed to get high yields and soil conservation practices are needed in order to prevent soil erosion.

Selected literature: FAO (1976a).

3.24 Acrisols

These soils have a distinct argillic B horizon, and a low base saturation (V

$<50\%$). They are real old tropical soils of regions with a dry and wet season, a monsoon climate. By leaching for a very long period, they are exhausted, with a low base saturation, and the content of weatherable minerals is generally very low. Consequently these soils are chemically poor, and physically the argillic B horizon limits root distribution. Normal Acrisols are the *Orthic Acrisols*. Those with plinthite within 125 cm of the surface are *Plinthic Acrisols;* those with hydromorphic properties in the upper 50 cm are *Gleyic Acrisols*. Some may have an umbric A horizon and are called *Humic Acrisols*. Finally the Acrisols with ferric properties (coarse red mottles or nodules up to 2 cm in diameter or a CEC in clay (<24 me/100 g) are called *Ferric Acrisols* (Plate 11).

Most soils have poor chemical and sometimes rather poor physical properties. They are used for growing crops, but yields are rather low. Humic and Orthic Acrisols can be improved by adding some lime and fertilizers. The others have some other limitations, as can be learned from their characteristics. Deficiency of nitrogen is a general constraint of Acrisols. Especially the CEC of the surface soil is low. Sometimes the surface soil shows some podzolization. The subsurface soil may be toxic from Al, Mn and Fe. Acrisols are generally developed from acid parent material. Some are saturated with aluminium, particularly those in South America. Such soils can be improved by liming, often at high cost. Mostly there is a deficiency of trace nutrients too. The best use is forest or grazing land. Many Acrisols are highly susceptible to erosion and often the surface layers up to the argillic or plinthic horizon are eroded when forest is cut, and a new ochric A horizon develops in the upper part of the argillic B horizon.

Selected literature: Mohr et al. (1972); Sanchez (1973).

3.25 Luvisols

Again soils with a distinct argillic B horizon, but with a high base saturation (V $>50\%$) and therefore agriculturally better than the exhausted Acrisols. They mainly occur in subhumid areas. There are various types of Luvisols; eight groups have been distinguished. The normal ones are *Orthic Luvisols*. In the tropics, there are Luvisols with plinthite in the zone of 0 to 125 cm called *Plinthic Luvisols* (Plate 13). Those with ferric properties are *Ferric Luvisols*, and those with vertic properties are *Vertic Luvisols*. Especially in the subtropics, some Luvisols have a strong brown or red B horizon, *Chromic Luvisols* (Plate 14). In semi-arid regions, Luvisols may have a calcic horizon or concentration of powdery lime, *Calcic Luvisols*. Those with an albic E

Horizon are *Albic Luvisols,* and those with hydromorphic properties in the upper 50 cm are *Gleyic Luvisols.*

Most Luvisols are good for agriculture, except some with specific limiting factors, e.g. stoniness, steep slopes. Base saturation is good; most need fertilizers in order to get good yields. They are not exhausted and have weatherable minerals. The argillic B horizon may prevent a really good root distribution. In soils with a heavy-textured B horizon, permeability may be low. Luvisols are well known in temperate and subtropical regions; they do occur in the tropics. There they are rather young in comparison to Acrisols.

The reddish colour of subtropical Luvisols (mainly Chromic Luvisols, Plate 14) is caused by rubefaction, a process of reddening resulting from dehydration of iron compounds in the dry season. In the subtropics mainly goethite and in the tropics also haematite are formed. Other iron compounds are involved too.

3.26 Cambisols

Cambisols have a cambic B horizon (Plate 15) or an umbric A horizon. Some have only an umbric A horizon (more than 25 cm thick) and are called *Humic Cambisols.* These are similar to Chernozems and Kastanozems; however they have an umbric A horizon (V $< 50\%$), not a mollic horizon.

All other Cambisols are more important, particularly in the tropics. There all soils with a cambic B horizon and an ochric A horizon are Cambisols. They are mostly rather young soils in comparison with other tropical soils, for example those that have an argillic, a natric or an oxic B horizon.

The B horizon of Cambisols is an altered horizon with a soil structure, or with some clay illuviation, or with a red colour, or with some evidence of removal of carbonates, or with some reduction processes. However all these alterations in the B horizon are not enough to qualify the B horizon, for instance as argillic, natric or oxic. Many Cambisols in the tropics and subtropics can be considered as soils in a transitional stage of development between very young soils and the older more mature soils like Acrisols, Planosols or Ferralsols. Consequently Cambisols may occur in various regions together with many of the major soils already mentioned. They are widespread in mountainous tropical areas with humid climates, except the Eutric Cambisols that occur mainly in subhumid regions. In the subtropics, Cambisols are more common. Another significant characteristic of Cambisols is texture, which is finer than very fine sand or loamy very fine sand. So all soils with a B horizon of coarse texture are excluded. These are Arenosols (Section 3.8), or Podzols if they have a spodic B horizon.

There are *Vertic Cambisols* (showing vertic characteristics), and *Calcic Cambisols* with a calcic or gypsic horizon or lime accumulation, but without a mollic A horizon; otherwise such soils would qualify as Chernozems. Those Cambisols with ferralic properties are *Ferralic Cambisols;* if they had a real oxic B horizon, they would be Ferralsols. *Chromic Cambisols* are strongly brown or red (rubefaction), but without a real argillic B horizon; they are therefore not Chromic Luvisols. Finally there are *Dystric Cambisols* (V $< 50\%$; Plate 15), *Eutric Cambisols* (V $> 50\%$), and *Gleyic Cambisols,* with hydromorphic properties in the zone 0-100 cm. Most Cambisols are good for agriculture if there are no specific limiting factors such as stoniness or steep slopes.

3.27 Some general remarks

Only a limited set of soil properties is used to separate the various major soils. Although such properties are useful also for agricultural evaluation of soils, they are not sufficient to characterize each soil or to determine its potentialities for growing crops, trees or grass. Therefore only some general ideas on the agricultural value of the major soils could be given. In practice, there are many exceptions.

The definitions and descriptions given are not complete. Special attention is paid to main properties and parts of definitions are neglected; otherwise this book would not be an introduction. Although the various soils in this chapter are given in the same sequence as in the official key, the subdivisions are not and so, this chapter cannot be used to classify soils according to the major soils of the soil map of the world. To do so, the official FAO book (Volume 1) must be used. Some groups of minor importance for the tropics or subtropics are not mentioned at all, for example those indicating permafrost, a frozen subsoil as found in areas with an arctic climate. They do occur exceptionally in high mountains in the tropics. Moreover some groups that hardly occur in the tropics or subtropics are not mentioned.

To learn the distribution of the various major soils of the world, the FAO/Unesco Soil Map of the World should be studied. The total areas and proportions are given in Section 3.29. The distribution in the tropics is not exactly known, a rough estimate has been made.

Selected literature: FAO/Unesco (1971-1978).

3.28 Intergrades

The descriptions of soils generally refer to typical representative soils of each major group. However, included in each unit are soils with variations in characteristics. Mostly there are gradual transitions in properties and consequently it is often difficult to determine exactly which of the major soils a particular soil belongs to, and how it has to be classified. Very often an 'intergrade', being a transitional soil between two or more other soils, is studied in the field. One example is given here. A typical Nitosol has properties as described in Section 3.23. However there are also intergrades towards some Acrisols, Luvisols, Ferralsols, and Cambisols. Some Dystric Nitosols and Orthic Acrisols may have almost identical properties. There is an intergrade when, for example, the argillic B horizon has transitional properties. A similar intergrade may exist between Eutric Nitosols and Orthic Luvisols. There are also intergrades between some Nitosols and Rhodic Ferralsols, especially if the argillic B horizon is not distinct, often because of deep biological homogenization of those soils, and if the amount of weatherable minerals in the Nitosols is rather low. A similar intergrade exists between some Nitosols and Ferralic Cambisols if the amount of weatherable minerals is higher and the argillic B horizon has minimum development. The consequence is that many intergrades are observable in the field.

Often it is only possible to decide which major soil a particular soil belongs to after various analyses (e.g. V, CEC, clay minerals, weatherable minerals). As long as not all relevant information is collected, which is a normal situation, various soil scientists will have different opinions on classification and consequently the same soil is sometimes classified differently. Fortunately crops have no idea about soil classification problems! Crops mostly react more to other soil properties, particularly to environmental conditions and farm management. If soil classifications are made for practical purposes, many soil properties not discussed in this chapter might be more relevant than those mentioned. To understand soils and to exchange knowledge and experience, one should try to classify soils as well as possible. However it is not always necessary nor possible to determine exactly all relevant soil properties for soil classification alone. As explained in Section 2.5, preference is given to limiting real systematic classification work to a few standard soils, called 'benchmark soils'. These might be representative good soils and other soils that occupy large areas. Mostly it is not necessary to investigate minor soils in detail and to do all analytical work on all soil samples. Most soil reports contain much more analytical data than are really needed or used.

3.29   Area of major soils

In the reports belonging to the Soil Map of the World, the area of major soils, and of associate major soils included in the map units is given in tables. A summary of the area of major soils, including the associations in which they are dominant, is presented in Table 2 for the world and in Table 3 for the tropics.

Table 2.   Major soil units of the world.

Major soil unit	Total		Potential cropland	
	area (million ha)	proportion (%)	area (million ha)	proportion (%)
Acrisols, Nitosols	1050	8.0	300	9
Andosols	101	0.8	80	2
Cambisols	925	7.0	500	15
Chernozems, Greyzems, Phaeozems	408	3.1	200	6
Ferralsols	1068	8.1	450	14
Fluvisols	316	2.4	250	8
Gleysols	623	4.7	250	8
Histosols	240	1.8	10	0
Lithosols, Rendzinas, Rankers	2264	17.2	0	0
Luvisols	922	7.0	650	20
Planosols	120	0.9	20	1
Podzols	478	3.6	130	4
Podzoluvisols	264	2.0	100	3
Regosols, Arenosols	1330	10.1	30	1
Solonchaks, Solonetz	268	2.0	50	2
Vertisols	311	2.4	150	5
Xerosols, Kastanozems	896	6.8	100	3
Yermosols	1176	8.9	0	0
Miscellaneous land units	420	3.2	0	0
Total	13180		3270	

Table 3. Major soil units of the tropics.

Major soil unit	Total		Useful	
	area (million ha)	proportion (%)	area (million ha)	proportion (%)
Acrisols	800	16	100	8
Andosols	80	2	70	6
Cambisols	100	2	60	5
Ferralsols	1050	21	350	28
Fluvisols	200	4	130	10
Gleysols	200	4	50	4
Histosols	100	2	10	1
Lithosols	900	18	0	0
Luvisols	200	4	150	12
Nitosols	250	5	200	16
Phaeozems	10	0	0	0
Planosols	70	1	10	1
Regosols	100	2	10	1
Solonchaks	40	1	10	1
Vertisols	200	4	50	4
Xerosols	400	8	50	4
Yermosols	200	4	0	0
Other soils	100	2	10	1
Total	5000		1260	

Table 3 suggests that about a quarter of all tropical land is potentially suitable for cultivation. Two-thirds of this land belongs to four major soil units: Ferralsols, Nitosols, Luvisols and Fluvisols. More exact figures for continents and countries can be taken from the tables in the FAO/Unesco reports.

4 Soil formation

4.1 Factors

The various factors of soil formation (parent material, climate, vegetation, topography, time, man, gravity and groundwater) are discussed in most books on soil science. They are equally relevant to soils in the tropics and subtropics, but they act differently there from in temperate regions. The main reason is that climate and consequently vegetation are different. In the humid tropics, where temperature is always high and rather constant (26 °C), weathering and biological processes are much more intense than in temperate regions. Many processes are more active and continuous. In tropical and subtropical regions with real dry periods almost all processes stop when soils are dry.

In semi-arid regions with a cool rainy season and a hot dry season as in parts of the subtropics, soil formation is similar to that of the temperate regions. However in semi-arid regions in the tropics, the rainy season is warm and soil formation is similar to that in the wet tropics, although it is less intensive and most processes stop during a long dry season. In tropical regions with a monsoon climate, many processes slow down in the drier season. As temperature decreases with altitude (about 0.6 °C per 100 m), the climate in tropical mountain areas becomes cooler and may become temperate or even boreal or arctic, but there is hardly any difference to compare with summer and winter of temperate regions of the Northern hemisphere.

Various chemical processes are different too. For example in moist tropical soils, ionization of water is much higher, silica is much more soluble, solution proceeds much quicker, and decomposition of organic matter is faster than in temperate regions.

It is a pity that major differences in soil climate are not indicated on the Soil Map of the World, particularly for those major soils that occur almost worldwide, e.g. Luvisols and Cambisols. Some major soils like Yermosols and Ferralsols, respectively typical for desert and wet tropical regions, reflect typical climatic conditions.

The various processes of soil formation will not be dealt with. They are well described in the book of Mohr, van Baren and van Schuylenborgh (1972). Here the various soil horizons and specific properties that characterize the major soils will be discussed, and only a general idea is given of their formation.

4.2 Soil horizons

Most soils have horizons, which are layers of soil almost parallel to the surface with characteristics resulting from processes of soil formation. The following master horizons are used to characterize the major soils of the world.

H horizon Consisting of organic material, deposited on the surface. The content of organic matter is >30% in clay soils, and >20% in sandy soils. Such a horizon consists of peat material of various composition, depending on the type of vegetation from which the organic material results. It can form only in anaerobic conditions, when soils are continuously waterlogged.

O horizon Also an organic surface horizon formed from accumulated organic matter deposited on the surface, but not saturated with water, e.g. an organic layer on top of a tropical forest soil. It generally consists of partly decomposed organic material.

A horizon A mineral surface horizon in which humified organic matter has accumulated. Therefore this horizon is somewhat darker than the underlying B horizon. The decomposed organic material is mixed with mineral material by biological activity (Plates 7, 10 and 15).

E horizon An eluvial horizon beneath an H, O or A horizon with a lower content of organic matter and a lighter colour, and having a concentration of quartz sand and silt or other unweatherable minerals. This horizon is formed by loss of iron or aluminium or fine clay, which have been transported and accumulated in the underlying B horizon. Sand grains, if any, are bleached (Plates 6 and 8).

B horizon A subsurface mineral horizon characterized by an illuvial concentration of fine clay (Bt), iron (Bs), aluminium (Bs) or humus (Bh), alone or in combination. It is also characterized by a relative accumulation of sesquioxides (as in Ferralsols) or by an alteration of the soil material that has a blocky or prismatic structure or a more intensive colour (Bw). This indicates that there are several types of B horizons to be discussed in the Section 4.3.

C horizon The deeper subsoil material, generally the parent material, that is hardly influenced by processes of soil formation. Mostly the material of this horizon is somewhat altered by weathering processes. There is a gradual transition from the B to the C horizon (Plates 6 and 15).

R horizon   The layer of indurated rock. In fact this is not a real soil horizon.

There are some other *letter suffixes* often used in soil descriptions e.g.
c for accumulation of concretions
g for mottling as a result of alternating oxidation and reduction
k for accumulation of calcium carbonate
n for accumulation of sodium
p for a part of the A horizon that is mixed by ploughing
q for accumulation of silica
r for strong reduction by groundwater
y for accumulation of gypsum
z for accumulation of soluble salts other than gypsum.

In the various systems of soil description, horizons are sometimes indicated by other letters and suffixes.

4.3 Diagnostic horizons

Diagnostic horizons are used to identify soil units. They have quantitatively defined properties and are the same as those adopted in Soil Taxonomy. The main characteristics are given only.

Histic H horizon   To be used to separate soils with an organic surface layer (>20 and <60 cm thick) from those with mineral surface soils. It has 28% or more organic matter if the mineral part has $>60\%$ clay, and 14% or more organic matter if the mineral part is sand (intermediate proportions for soils with intermediate clay content). A histic H horizon is formed under waterlogged conditions, often to be found in soils of depressions that are wet the whole year round.

Mollic A horizons   A thick dark horizon with a high base saturation (V $>50\%$), and a strong soil structure. It is more than 25 cm thick in normal soils, and the organic matter content is $>1\%$. It is diagnostic for Chernozems and Kastanozems often formed in grass steppes (dense and rather deep rootsystem). Organic matter is thoroughly mixed with mineral material. Many such soils are frozen in winter and rather dry in summer; consequently there is less leaching than normal. Mollic A horizons almost do not occur in the

54

tropics. They are typical for continental parts of the subtropics.

Umbric A horizon A horizon similar to the mollic A horizon, except for base saturation, which is < 50%. It is diagnostic for non-calcareous soils, for example in Andosols where some have a mollic A horizon (Mollic Andosols) and others an umbric A horizon (Humic Andosols, Plate 4). A similar subdivision is also made in Gleysols and Planosols.

Ochric A   horizon The most common surface horizon without the characteristics of a histic H, a mollic A, or an umbric A horizon. As most soils in the tropics do not have such horizons, they generally have an ochric A horizon. Such a horizon is the first to develop in soils (Plates 7, 10 and 15). If there is fresh soil material and vegetation starts to grow, roots penetrate soils in the upper layer. Dead roots and leaves decompose, forming some organic matter and a colloidal part that is rather stable (humus) remains in the soil. Micro-organisms play a large role in this process. The upper layer turns a somewhat darker colour than the other part of the soil and often structural elements are formed. In most soils, the amount and type of organic matter is in equilibrium with environmental conditions.

An ochric horizon is diagnostic for Arenosols and Regosols, both are very young soils. It is moreover characteristic for Xerosols and Yermosols. Formation of these soils is extremely slow, because they are almost always completely dry and have only a very sparse vegetation of short grasses. Therefore the ochric A horizon in these soil units is weakly (Xerosols) or very weakly (Yermosols) developed. Very weak means less than 0.5% organic matter in sandy soils and < 1% in clayey soils in the upper 40 cm soil layer. A weak ochric A horizon has more organic matter but still less than 1%. In this way, attempts are made to distinguish soils developed in a real arid climate (Yermosols) from those developed in a climate with a short rainy season (Xerosols).

Argillic B horizon An important subsurface horizon, because it is diagnostic for various major soil units. It is a horizon in which clay particles have accumulated from the upper soil layer (A or E), and that have filled pores and other openings. Mostly fine clay particles have been translocated and settled (illuviated) in the B horizon in a very thin layer on the surface of structural elements (peds) (Plates 10 and 14). A considerable amount of clay has to be translocated before a real argillic B horizon is formed. This often takes a long time and consequently an argillic B horizon is diagnostic of well developed older soils. Depending on the soil parent material and the environmental conditions somewhat different argillic B horizons can be observed in the field. It is often difficult to detect the various characteristics, particularly clay skins or clay coatings (the very thin fine clay deposits on ped surfaces), even when a hand lens is used. So thin sections are often made in a laboratory, and studied microscopically. Another difficulty is that some parts of the argillic B horizon are altered by other processes (e.g. biological homogenization), and the typical skin characteristics have disappeared. For these and other reasons, the complete definition of an argillic B horizon occupies several pages.

The main properties are as follows:

a the increase in clay content occurs within a vertical distance of 30 cm

b in sandy soils it contains at least 3% more clay than the eluvial (upper) horizon

c in clay soils it contains at least 8% more clay than the eluvial horizon

d in sandy soils it is > 15 cm and in clay soils > 7.5 cm thick

e there are clay skins on ped surfaces, and in pores. In most tropical clay soils (kaolinitic clays), clay skins occur at least in the lower part of the B horizon.

Translocation of fine clay from the A into the B horizon (argillation) is a complicated process influenced by various factors such as mineralogical composition, type of clay and organic matter, chemical, physical, biological, and environmental conditions. In the tropics and subtropics, argillic B horizons often occur in older soils that are alternately moist and dry. Such conditions are typical for a climate with wet and dry seasons. In a very early stage of the wet season, when dry soils suddenly become wet, fine clay particles can be translocated. As soon as a soil is completely moist, less clay particles are translocated. In real kaolinitic clay soils without weatherable minerals (Ferralsols), clay particles are partly cemented by sequioxides and although clay content may be high, only a small fraction is dispersable in water. Moreover such soils are mainly formed in permanent humid tropical regions, and so conditions are less favourable for the formation of an argillic B horizon.

In tropical and subtropical regions, Nitosols, Acrisols and Luvisols are the main soils for which an argillic B horizon is diagnostic. A really distinct argillic B horizon occurs in Acrisols and Luvisols. The difference between the two is base saturation, which is (at least in a part of the B horizon) less than 50% in Acrisols and more than 50% is Luvisols. Though the limit is arbitrary, the idea is to separate the real exhausted Acrisols with little weatherable minerals from those that have more favourable conditions, the Luvisols. In Soil Taxonomy, the Ultisols (to be compared with Acrisols here) and the Alfisols (to be compared with the Luvisols) are also characterized by an argillic B horizon, but the limit for base saturation is 35% instead of 50% (Chapter 6). The Soil Map of the World also shows Nitosols, that have an argillic B horizon, which is less distinct (Section 3.23).

The presence of an argillic B horizon is considered important in characterizing and classifying soils. For agricultural evaluation of such soils, it is useful to know the presence, base saturation, and thickness. However it is also necessary to study in the field soil structure, texture, porosity, permeability, consistence and particularly presence and distribution of plant roots. Clay skins covering ped surfaces and filling pores in well developed argillic B horizons limit penetration of roots, movement of soil water and diffusion of air in the soil. In such a situation, roots are only found between the structure elements and although there may be an extensive root system, roots cannot penetrate and do not profit from much of the volume of this soil horizon, namely the inner part of the soil peds. If, however, clay skins are not very clear and not very extensive, or if a part of the argillic B horizon is mixed by biological action, the soil volume available for the plant roots is much greater. So mere mention that an argillic horizon is present does not indicate enough to learn potentials for agriculture, except perhaps that Nitosols are better than Acrisols and that a high base saturation is more favourable than a low base saturation. Similarly, as fine clay particles are moved from the A horizon into the B horizon, some organic matter can also migrate to the B horizon. Consequently there is in some soils a B horizon rather rich in organic matter, e.g. some Humic Acrisols, Humic Nitosols and Solodic Planosols (Plate 8).

Natric B horzion   This has all the properties of an argillic B horizon and in addition an exchangeable sodium percentage (ESP) of more than 15%. It is a characteristic horizon for Solonetz, explained in Section 3.15. In older Solonetz, a solodization process takes place. The natric B horizon is rather dense and has a clear prismatic or even columnar structure. The result is a bleaching of sand and silt grains, because the grains lose their thin coatings. The eluvial horizon on top of the argillic horizon becomes grayer or even whitish-gray, and tongues of that horizon penetrate the B horizon between the coarse prisms or columns. If such a process continues, a Solodic Planosol (Section 3.14) with a distinct albic E horizon (Section 4.3) is formed (Plate 8).

Cambic B horizon   An altered subsurface horizon (Plate 15) with the following main properties:
a soil texture is very fine sand, loamy very fine sand or finer (so altered horizons in coarser-textured sandy material are never cambic horizons; soils having such a coarse-textured B horizon are Arenosols or Spodosols)
b the horizon has structure
c there is $>3\%$ weatherable mineral material and CEC of clay fraction >16

meq per 100 g

d the soil material has been altered; for instance clay content is higher than in the C horizon, or the colour is redder than that of the C horizon, or part of the carbonates present in the parent material is removed and accumulated in an underlying horizon, and finally there may be evidence of reduction.

Some minor special properties are neglected. Cambic B horizons are horizons with weatherable minerals (otherwise the B horizon could be an oxic B horizon; see below). Its material has been altered in a simple way, and it has structure. It may also have some extra clay particles, but not enough to be an argillic horizon. The clay increase in a cambic B horizon is often caused by weathering of mineral material resulting in formation of new clay minerals. A redder colour is caused by alteration of iron compounds and removal of carbonates by percolating water. If percolation water does not flow to deeper layers or to groundwater, carbonates accumulate in subsoils that dry out in the dry season. In the non-calcareous soils, reddening or rubefaction is more common.

Most cambic B horizons are favourable horizons, because they have good physical properties and roots may penetrate everywhere. Water retention depends on soil texture and porosity. Chemical properties vary widely and depend on mineral composition.

Spodic B horizon A subsurface horizon, more than 2.5 cm thick, cemented by a combination of organic matter with iron or aluminium of both. It is a humus-iron pan, in the Northern hemisphere well known in real Podsols. In the tropics, such soils (Section 3.12) occur only in very poor quartz material.

Oxic B horizon A typic subsurface horizon of tropical soils (Plate 7). The main properties are as follows:

a it is at least 30 cm thick, usually more than 1 or 2 m thick

b it has only traces of weatherable minerals, therefore mineral weathering has been completed

c the texture is sandy loam or finer (>15% clay) (soils with a similar B horizon but a coarse texture are Ferralic Arenosols)

d CEC of clay fraction <16 me per 100 g, indicating clay of the kaolinitic clay group

e it has gradual or diffuse boundaries between soil horizons; so the whole soil does not show much differentiation. The soil has almost uniform properties to a depth of a few metres. The oxic B horizon has good physical properties, is not heavy-textured, is porous and very permeable and roots can penetrate the whole soil. However chemically such a soil is poor, not only because there are

58

no weatherable minerals but also because the CEC is low. Moreover many oxisols may have a high percentage of adsorbed aluminium that can be toxic for plant roots.

These natural limitations are important when soils with an oxic B horizon are cultivated. Without fertilizers, yields are always low. With fertilizers, yields often increase considerably (Section 3.13).

Calcic horizon A horizon of accumulation of calcium carbonate (lime). It mostly occurs in B or C horizons, the thickness is more than 15 cm and lime content is 15% or more (at least 5 percentage units more than in the C horizon). It is a typical horizon in soils of arid and semi-arid regions, in which only a small amount of rainwater penetrates to a shallow depth. If this percolating water were to flow to deep layers, no calcic horizon could develop (Plate 9).

Sometimes there is accumulation of lime that does not meet the requirements of a calcic horizon (powdery lime or lime mycelium). Even non-calcareous soils can have lime accumulation or a calcic horizon, for example when fresh calcareous desert dust is deposited on these soils.

The depth of the calcic horizon or the horizon of lime accumulation is an indication of soil moisture conditions during the rainy season, taking into account other soil properties that determine water retention such as permeability and drainability. As soil moisture is the main limiting factor for natural grasses and dry farming, the depth of these horizons is a useful characteristic for evaluation of soils in semi-arid regions.

Gypsic horizon Similar to a calcic horizon, but with accumulation of gypsum (calcium sulphate) instead of lime. Here too, the thickness should be more than 15 cm and it should have more than 5% more gypsum than in the underlying C horizon. The product of the thickness of the layer (in cm) and the content of gypsum (in %) should be 150 or more. If less, it is a horizon of gypsum accumulation. A gypsic horizon often occurs in soils also having a calcic horizon. As gypsum is somewhat more soluble than calcium carbonate the gypsic horizon or some accumulation of gypsum is found at a greater depth than the calcic horizon.

Sulphuric horizon A horizon characterized by a very low pH (<3.5) and yellowish mottles of jarosite when the soil material is in a stage of oxidation. A sulphuric horizon is characteristic for Thionic Fluvisols. They are typical of non-calcareous sediments in brackish or marine water (Section 3.4).

Albic E horizon   A very light-coloured (whitish or light gray) sandy horizon, mostly consisting of uncoated sand and silt grains. It overlies a spodic B, argillic B or natric B horizon or an almost impervious clay layer. It is a highly degraded soil horizon from which clay particles and iron oxides have been removed (Plate 8). In Podzols (Section 3.12), it overlies a spodic B horizon (Plate 6), which, in tropical regions, may be found at a depth of some metres and all the coarse quartz sand to a few metres depth consists of albic material. Such very infertile soils are often called 'white sands'. Albic E horizons are diagnostic for Planosols (Section 3.14).

4.4   Diagnostic soil properties

Besides the diagnostic horizons, there are also some soil properties used to separate major soils. The most important are mentioned below.

Albic material   The material of an albic E horizon, mainly light-coloured un-coated quartz sand material (Plate 6).

Aridic moisture regime   Indicating very dry soils of arid regions (Xerosols and Yermosols). Soils with an aridic moisture regime are completely dry except of 90 consecutive days in the subtropics and for 60 consecutive days in the tropics (Section 4.5)

Ferralic properties   They are properties of soils that are almost Ferralsols, but the texture is too coarse and therefore they are classified as a Ferralic group in Cambisols and Arenosols.

Ferric properties   They indicate the distinct red mottles and weakly cemented or iron indurated red nodules up to 2 cm diameter in tropical soils (Luvisols and Acrisols).

Gilgai microrelief   In association with Vertisols (Section 3.3), consisting of small shallow micro-basins and micro-knolls in level areas (Figure 2), and of micro-valleys and micro-ridges on slopes.

High content of organic matter in the B horizon   (in Humic Ferralsols, Acrisols and Nitosols) means $\geqslant 1.35\%$ organic matter to a depth of 100 cm.

High salinity   The electrical conductivity is more than 15 $EC_e. 10^3$ within 125 cm for sandy soils and 75 cm for clay soils (Section 3.5 and Plate 2).

Hydromorphic properties   They are related to an alternately low and high groundwater, causing alternate oxidation and reduction in this soil zone. The lower part of the soil is continuously reduced, and is gray or bluish-gray. In the zone of fluctuating groundwater, reddish and orange mottles caused by segregrated iron compounds occur in a matrix of reduced soil. In the upper part of this zone and in the capillary zone the matrix is formed by oxidized compounds with some spots of reduced material. In various soils with different mineralogical composition and with different processes of soil formation, reduction and oxidation, colours are somewhat different and therefore the complete definition of hydromorphic properties is long and complicated. Much depends on type and amount of iron, clay and organic matter. In soils with stagnating water over an impermeable layer, similar phenomena occur. Besides iron, manganese (small dark spots) plays a role. Often there are small iron-manganese concretions.

Hydromorphic properties characterize Gleysols (Section 3.6 and Plate 3) and gleyic groups in various other major soils if these properties occur in the upper 50 cm of a soil. As these properties are extremely useful for agricultural evaluation of soils, various subclasses can be distinguished when soils are investigated and mapped in more detail. The subclasses refer to four or five classes of depths below the soil surface, and to the intensity of the mottling. It is worthwile to measure the fluctuation of groundwater at specific time intervals during a year in combination with precipitation.

Plinthite and ironstone   Plinthite is clayey soil material in a zone with intense red mottles related to blocky structural elements. It is rich in iron compounds and poor in organic matter. The dinstinct reddish to purple mottles in a bluish-gray matrix are produced by fluctuating groundwater (Plate 12). Sesquioxides are mobilized, transported over a short distance and accumulated. In moist soil, plinthite can be cut with a knife. If it dries out, the material hardens irreversibly and is then called ironstone. This hardening is often the result of a lowered groundwater table, e.g. during a geological upheavel of the terrain, or if land is artificially drained. Plinthite also hardens on exposure in road cuts. Ironstone often occurs as a hardpan (Plate 14) that is sometimes several metres thick. It can also consist of irregular aggregates or a cluster of aggregates forming ironstone concretions (Plate 13). Such concretions are often eroded and deposited elsewhere (Plate 11), forming a concretional ironstone layer that no longer has any association with the original plinthite. Such soils are indicated as a petric phase. In soils in which ironstone is formed in situ, the hardened material grades into real plinthite in deeper soil layers (Plate 13). Many ironstone hardpans at or near the soil surface are old. The overlying soil material has been eroded. Ironstone concretional material is often used for paving roads, the red roads of the tropics. In some countries, the clayey plinthite is cut in blocks, and dried in the sun. They are used, for instance, to built houses, walls and temples. Ironstone was formerly called 'laterite'.

One of the most common misunderstandings about tropical soils is that almost all tropical soils will harden upon exposure to solar radiation, e.g. when forests are cut. Ironstone is formed only from plinthite. The total area in which it can be formed in or near the surface is estimated at some 7% of real tropical soils. The most extensive areas with ironstone pans are in Africa, mainly in older landscapes.

In the tropics, plinthite and ironstone occur in various major soils. In the subtropics, it can occur in older soils that have had tropical conditions in former geological periods (Plate 14).

Sulphidic material is material as described for the sulphuric horizon (Section 4.3). Like a sulphuric horizon, it is toxic but it does not show jarosite mottles.

4.5 Soil moisture and temperature regimes

Although a differentiation of soils according to their moisture and temperature regimes is not given for the Soil Map of the World these characteristics are so important, in particular for agriculture, that the different regimes are mentioned here. The descriptions cover the main characteristics. Details are given in Soil Taxonomy, (Soil Survey Staff, 1975). An example is shown in Figure 4.

Soil moisture regimes
Soil moisture regimes are a general indication of soil moisture conditions. They roughly indicate the periods when soils are dry or moist, and refer to moisture in the soil control section, which is the zone between 10 and 30 cm depth in clayey, and between 30 and 90 cm in sandy soils. There are six classes of soil moisture regime:

peraquic groundwater is always near the surface

aquic groundwater reaches into the subsoil (Plate 3)

aridic and torric soils are mostly dry; they may be moist for a period up to 90 consecutive days (in arid climates, Plate 9)

udic soils are mostly moist, they may be dry for less than 90 consecutive days (in humid climates, Plate 11)

ustic soils are moist for more than half a year and dry for up to 90 days

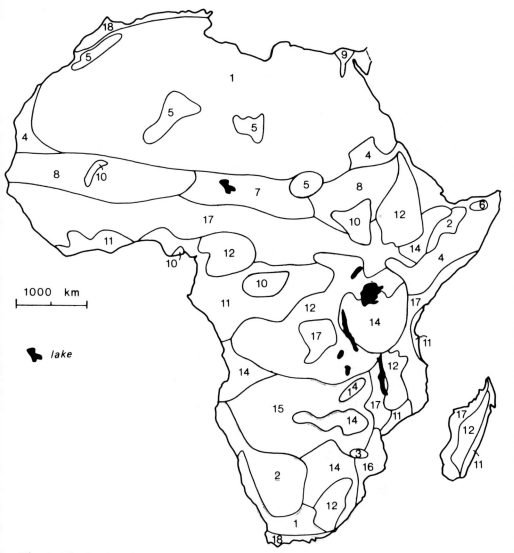

Fig. 4. Distribution of soil moisture and soil temperature regimes in Africa.

1. aridic, thermic
2. aridic, isothermic
3. aridic, hyperthermic
4. aridic, isohyperthermic
5. aridic, mesic and frigid
6. aridic to ustic, thermic
7. aridic to ustic, hyperthermic
8. aridic to ustic, isohyperthermic
9. aquic, thermic
10. aquic, isohyperthermic
11. udic, isohyperthermic
12. udic to ustic, thermic
13. udic to ustic, isohyperthermic
14. ustic, thermic
15. ustic, isothermic
16. ustic, hyperthermic
17. ustic, isohyperthermic
18. xeric, thermic

(tropical monsoon climate, Plate 10)

xeric soils are moist in the cool winter season and dry in the growing (summer) season (Mediterranean type of climate, Plate 14).

In arid regions, a dry season or a dry month refers to a period almost without any precipitation. Soils are dry; there is no water available for plant growth. In tropical regions, a dry month indicates a period during which precipitation is much less than evatranspiration. This is mostly characterized by precipation less than 100 mm. Some specialists have set this limit at 60 mm. About three quarters of the tropics has a pronounced dry season and a quarter has no dry season.

Soil temperature regimes

Soil temperature regimes are important for plant growth, they roughly indicate the temperature in the root zone at a depth of 50 cm. There are several soil temperature classes, characterized by the mean annual soil temperature (mean) and by the difference between the mean summer and winter soil temperature (differences), in degrees Celsius.

frigid	mean < 8 °C	difference >5 °C
mesic	mean > 8 °C and <15 °C	difference >5 °C
thermic	mean >15 °C and <22 °C	difference >5 °C
hyperthermic	mean >22 °C	difference >5 °C
isofrigid	mean < 8 °C	difference <5 °C
isomesic	mean > 8 °C and <15 °C	difference <5 °C
isothermic	mean >15 °C and <22 °C	difference <5 °C
isohyperthermic	mean >22 °C	difference <5 °C

In the humid tropics, isohyperthermic soil temperature regimes are common, except at higher altitudes where isothermic and even isomesic or frigid soil temperatures may occur. In the subtropics, the difference between the mean summer and winter soil temperature is more than 5 °C and thermic soil temperature regimes are common; the others may occur too.

4.6 Other useful soil properties

There are many other useful soil properties not mentioned before and not used to differentiate major soils on the Soil Map of the World, because they cannot be shown on such a small-scale map. Some are mentioned below.

Rooting depth and volume It is useful to measure the depth to which plant roots can penetrate. Sometimes roots go deep but only part of the soil can be penetrated. An example was given in the description of the argillic B horizon (Section 4.3), in which prismatic structural elements are covered by clay skins so that roots cannot penetrate those parts of a soil. Then the rooting volume is much smaller than the total soil volume in which roots are observed. Therefore besides rooting depth, rooting volume is a useful property for evaluating agricultural potentiality. Many soil properties prevent plant roots from penetrating the subsoil, e.g. hardpans, platy structures, stratified layers, high aluminium adsorption.

Stratification In various soils deposited by water or wind, very fine layers occur, each only one or a few millimetres thick. They indicate that this part of the soil has not been disturbed since it was deposited and that roots have not penetrated to that depth (Plates 1 and 16).

Content of organic matter A useful soil characteristic that influences for instance, stability of soil structure, microbial activity and soil fertility. Content of organic matter is relatively high in soils under tropical forest and high grass savannas. In such soils, the content of organic matter is stable; decomposition is equal to formation of new organic matter. If such soils are cultivated, the content decreases and after some years or decades a new equilibrium is reached.

Base saturation (V) The percentage of bases on the soil adsorbing complex. The cation-exchange capacity (CEC) of tropical soils is low because of the low exchange capacity of kaolinitic clay minerals, which are typical for tropical soils. Soils with a high base saturation are preferred for agriculture. Most older agricultural regions have soils with a high base saturation. Soils with a low value are deficient of major essential plant nutrients. Often aluminium is present at too high a proportion on the exchange complex, causing toxicity that can be corrected by mixing soils with lime. Soils with a low base saturation and with Al toxicity occur over large areas in Latin and Central America and less in Africa and Asia. The main reason is probably that most African soils get some calcareous dust from the Sahara and Kalahari deserts. Many Asian soils have been rejuvenated by volcanic ash.

Homogenization This is a process by which the soil material is thoroughly mixed by biological activity (biological homogenization) or by mechanical internal processes like cracking and self-mulching in Vertisols (mechanical homogenization). Biological homogenization is an extremely important process, because it improves soil structure, mixes mineral and organic material and increases soil porosity and internal drainage. It is caused by the action of plant roots, and soil flora and fauna. Worms, and, in the tropics particularly, ants and termites are important in this respect. Through the high and almost constant soil temperature, biological activity in tropical soils is more than double that in temperate soils. It is greatly reduced during dry seasons.

Truncated and buried soils In many soils, the material is not a product of weathering of rock in situ. Often the material has been removed from one site and deposited elsewhere. Consequently various soils are truncated, that means the upper part of the soil has been eroded and the B or C horizon is now at the surface. Later a new A horizon, often an ochric A horizon, is formed in the former B horizon. Such a horizon often has somewhat different properties from a normal A horizon.

In other parts of a landscape, removed soil material is deposited on top of an existing soil. Such a layer can be some decimetres or even more than a metre thick. The soil profile shows two soils. The lowest soil, the original one, is the buried soil. It is useful to study the effect of such deposits on the rooting depth and volume.

Cumulic soils Some soils have a thick A horizon, because there has been a gradual increase in thickness by a very thin annual deposit of new soil material that is directly incorporated in the A horizon.

Palaeosols Soils formed under former climatic and vegetational conditions that are different from the present condition. They show characteristics of the old conditions, e.g. soils with many properties of real humid tropics, now found in drier parts of the tropics or in the subtropics.

Crusts Cemented layers at or near the surface. The cementing agent may, for instance, be lime, gypsum, iron or silica. A cemented calcic horizon is a petrocalcic horizon; a cemented gypsic horizon, a petrogypsic horizon; an iron-cemented layer is an ironpan or indurated iron layer; and a silica-cemented layer is a duripan. Such a crust highly impedes root development. If crusts are at the surface, because the overlying layer has been eroded, run-off is high.

In desert regions, a surface crust or surface seal (a brittle crust 1 or 2 mm thick) is common. It hampers infiltration of rainwater.

Mineral composition   The composition of various kind of minerals, particularly of weatherable minerals, that produce plant nutrients. In most old tropical soils, these are little weatherable minerals, if any, which together with a low supply of nitrogen is one of the main reasons for low yields. Weathering products of basic or intermediate rock material supply more suitable nutrients than acid rock material.

The main clay minerals in tropical soils are the 1:1 lattice clays like kaolinite and halloysite. In Vertisols, the 2:1 lattice clay montmorillonite is the characteristic clay material. In Andosols, allophane (amorphous aluminiosilicate) is dominant. Gibbsite, $Al(OH)_3$, occurs in some tropical soils. In various subtropical soils, illite (also a 2:1 lattice clay) occurs, often together with kaolinite.

Selected literature: FAO/Unesco (1971-1978); FAO (1973a); Soil Science Soc. of America (1978); Soil Survey Staff (1951; 1975).

5 Soil conditions

5.1 Landscape types

There are a great many landscapes, also called landforms, land systems, land types, landscape types, such as river plains, deltas, uplands, mountains and deserts. They are characterized by topography, hydrology, vegetation or land use, climate and soil conditions. Soil scientists have to know environmental conditions, particularly geology and geomorphology, in order to understand soil formation, relations between various soils and their position. There are so many variations in soil-forming factors that everywhere soil conditions are different, even if landscape types are rather similar. This is one of the interesting aspects of soil science and it demonstrates the necessity of soil investigation in the field.

A few general aspects of some landscapes are discussed in the following sections and some common ones with major soil units are described. These landscapes occur in various climatic zones and therefore, for completeness, each one should be described for at least four or five of these zones. That, however, is beyond the scope of this book. Attention is given only to some general aspects. Often the soil conditions in a particular landscape are quite different from what is described here. Therefore it is instructive to study soil maps and reports of various regions to learn about the regional distribution of soils.

5.2 Soils of river valleys

Most river valleys consist of a river plain and some river terraces on either side of the plain. The highest terrace is bordered by uplands. The river plain has young soils (Fluvisols, Plate 1) with well drained soils on the levees along the river, and poorly drained soils in backswamps or basins at some distance. When land is not protected by dykes, it is flooded during periods of high river discharge. Levee soils also occur near former river beds. The older ones may consist of Cambisols. Natural fertility depends on the type of sediment, which is related to the weathered rock material of the whole catchment area.

If the upper part of such a catchment area (river drainage basin) is situated in the tropics, sediments are less fertile than when it is situated in a more temperate region. The material that is eroded from a tropical region consists of heavily weathered sediments, often also altered during some cycles of soil formation. In arid and semi-arid regions, many poorly drained soils are saline (Solonchaks and Solonetz). In the humid tropics, the poorly drained soils are generally used for growing rice and the levees for various crops.

Many rivers have three terraces. The highest and oldest terrace generally consists of gravelly material and is highly dissected. There are well developed soils. The middle terrace is less gravelly and less dissected and also has well developed soils. In the humid tropics, they can be Ferralsols and Acrisols, some with plinthite. In the subtropics, Luvisols are most common, whereas in arid and semi-arid regions Yermosols, Xerosols or Cambisols occurs often with Solonetz in slight depressions.

The soils of the lowest terrace are mainly deep soils with characteristics related to climatic conditions. Luvisols, Cambisols and Gleysols are common, in the tropics with ferralic or ferric properties.

Most river valleys are densely populated and soils are used intensively. Potential for agricultural use depends closely on hydrological conditions (floods), suitability for drainage or irrigation, salinity hazards (in arid regions), and soil fertility. Since cutting of forest in the upper part of most catchment areas increases, the discharges of rivers increase and it is often difficult to control floods. Reforestation and forest protection in river catchment areas are of utmost importance in many countries.

5.3 Soils of deltas and coastal areas

Almost all soils in these landscapes are influenced by high groundwater. There are small levees along river courses and near the coast beach walls that may have groundwater at a depth of some metres. A delta is characterized by a river that splits up in many branches. It is flooded when discharge of the river is high. The lower part of each branch is influenced by the tides and is called an estuary, which merges towards the sea in brackish and finally in a saline coastal zone. Peat can be formed in all continuously wet parts, especially when the climate is humid. Histosols are common; or soils may have a histic surface layer. The brackish zone is often characterized by Thionic Fluvisols, if the carbonate content of sedimented material is low. They occur over large areas in the deltas of many rivers in the tropics, including the Chao Phraya, Mekong and Orinoco rivers.

The beach walls in coastal areas can have Regosols, Cambisols (Plate 15) or Arenosols. If they consist of almost pure quartz, Podzols can occur. The wet backswamps consist of Humic Gleysols or Histosols. There too Thionic

1000 km

 lake

Fig. 5. Africa: Legend of the soil map, area of mapping units and or potential arable land

Symbol	Unit	Total land		Potential arable	
		area (million ha)	propor-tion (%)	area (million ha)	propor-tion (%)
A	Acrisols	42	1.4	18	3.0
B	Cambisols	104	3.5	46	7.6
E	Rendzinas[1]	3	0.1	0	0
F	Ferralsols	420	14.0	210	34.5
G	Gleysols	62	2.1	48	7.9
H	Phaeozems[1]	1	0.0	0	0
I	Lithosols	346	11.5	0	0
J	Fluvisols	73	2.4	50	8.2
K	Kastanozems	3	0.1	0	0
L	Luvisols	252	8.4	83	13.7
N	Nitosols	116	3.8	72	11.8
O	Histosols[1]	2	0.1	0	0
P	Podzols[1]	2	0.1	0	0
Q	Arenosols	408	13.6	0	0
R	Regosols	164	5.4	0	0
S	Solonetz	9	0.3	0	0
T	Andosols	5	0.2	3	0.5
V	Vertisols	98	3.3	78	12.8
W	Planosols	18	0.6	0	0
X	Xerosols	132	4.4	0	0
Y	Yermosols	482	16.0	0	0
Z	Solonchaks	16	0.5	0	0
I	Rock debris	31	1.0	0	0
D	Dunes	173	5.8	0	0
	Salt flats, others[1]	48	1.6	0	0
Total		3 010		608	

1. Not on the soil map.
The area of each mapping unit is given in FAO/Unesco Soil Map of the World, Vol. 6 Table 3. Each unit is an association. It therefore includes some other units and the figures do not represent the exact area. The simplified soil map is published with the permission of FAO and Unesco. The potential arable land area was estimated by the author, from all information available in Volume 6.

Fluvisols are found, except when the marine sediments are calcareous, but many tropical marine sediments are non-calcareous and fertility is generally much lower than in temperate coastal areas. The idea that all deltas and low coastal areas in the tropics have good potential for argriculture is wrong, because there are too large areas with Thionic Fluvisols and unripened mud clays (Section 3.4). Reclamation of Histosols is rather difficult too, because of rapid decomposition of organic matter and considerable subsidence of the land surface after drainage. Moreover fertilizer management is complex.

5.4 Soils of uplands

Uplands have an undulating or hilly topography and erosion of sloping land is a common feature. Consequently many soils on slopes have lost the surface A horizon and a new ochric A horizon has been developed in a former B horizon. The eroded material has been deposited in valleys and depressions that are wet during the rainy season.

Slopes are generally well drained; flat areas are less well or poorly drained. In a monsoon climate, they may have Planosols. In the humid tropics Ferralsols and Acrisols occur. Luvisols are common in the subtropics. Steep slopes often have Cambisols or Lithosols. In humid tropics, well drained rolling land also can have Nitosols. Vertisols and soils with vertic properties in the subsoils occur in lower parts. Land is flat or somewhat undulating. Erosion is often a serious problem, even on gently sloping land, because the infiltration rate of Vertisols is low. A combination is often found of Ferralsols and Acrisols on hills and Vertisols in the lower parts. Bases and silica have been leached from the hill soils. These accumulate in the lower parts of the landscape and give rise to montmorillonitic clays.

Buried soils often occur at the lower end of slopes. If conditions are suitable, plinthite is formed. By uplift of the landscape or lowering of the groundwater table, ironstone is formed. Many areas with a rather poor soil drainage have plinthite in subsoils, and if the overlying soil is eroded ironstone occurs near the surface. A new process of 'rock' weathering in ironstone may start. Various soils of uplands have a layer of ironstone concretions at some depth, and there is no plinthite below this layer, because these concretions originate from ironstone at higher altitudes, that has disintegrated, and has been eroded and deposited lower down. Later they have been covered with soil material.

In the subtropics, conditions are similar, soil formation is less intense and various types of Luvisols occur. Chromic Luvisols generally occur in regions with a Mediterranean type of climate (cool, rainy winters and dry summers).

Soil erosion, soil fertility and improvement of farm management are major aspects.

5.5 Soils of highlands and mountains

Soils of older stable land surfaces of considerable geological age develop on peneplanes, sloping lands, escarpments and real mountains. In the tropics, these peneplains mostly have Acrisols, sometimes Ferralsols. Cambisols are common on steep slopes, because of continuous erosion of the surface soil. Lithosols, Rankers and sometimes Rendzinas as well as Lithic phases of various soils may occur everywhere in these landscapes. Many peneplains have plinthite or ironstone. Thick ironstone layers, often called 'laterite caps', may characterize those peneplains. The caps show up in escarpments. In the mountain valleys, much younger soils are found.

Climate has changed during the various geological periods and consequently old soils have often developed in alternating climatic conditions characterized by different processes of soil formation. Such soils are Palaeosols. They often occur as buried soils in deeper substrata. In such a position, there are even some Ferralsols and Acrisols in Central Europe.

In mountainous regions, temperature decreases 0.5 or 0.6 °C with every hundred metres of altitude. At altitudes of 2000 m or more, soils similar to those in temperate regions and, at high altitudes, even soils with permafrost occur (a permanently frozen subsoil, Gelic soils such as Gelic Gleysols or Gelic Regosols). Many soils at higher altitudes, developed in a relatively cool and often humid climate, contain more organic matter than similar soils a bit further downhill. They represent the 'Humic' soils. Histosols, soils with a thin organic layer or soils with an umbric A horizon, are often present. Histosols are also formed on impermeable rock material.

The climate, particularly rainfall, is widely different on different sides of a mountain or mountain range. This is reflected in soil conditions.

In regions with volcanoes (Hawaii, Java, Central Africa, Andes), Andosols are common (Plate 4). There too differences in altitude and precipitation govern soil formation. In older volcanic landscapes, Andosols grade into Nitosols, Ferralsols and Acrisols. Volcanic ash has been and sometimes still is deposited in thin layers over very large areas around volcanoes. Rejuvenation of soils is common, because fresh volcanic ash is deposited and rejuvenates soils. Soils are often Nitosols and Ferric Luvisols in the tropics and Cambisols or Luvisols in the subtropics. Vitric Andosols occur near the top of the volcano and further afield in volcanic regions with an arid climate.

Agricultural potential in tropical highlands are generally low, except in valleys, in some plains and in volcanic regions if slopes are not too steep, otherwise an intricate pattern of small terraces has to be made. The good soils are suitable for many crops. The percentage of good soils, however, is usually very small except in volcanic mountainous areas, and transport of products to centres of population is difficult. Moreover, night frosts can damage crops. A serious problem is deforestation, followed by erosion and floods.

5.6 Soils of deserts and semi-deserts

Most soils are Yermosols and Xerosols. Solonchaks occur in depressions, and Fluvisols and Solonchaks in river valleys. Strong winds have blown away surface layers of large areas. In other areas, the material accumulates in dunes. Some are sand dunes, others are silt or clay dunes (Regosols), because carbonate and silica-cemented clay particles act like sand particles. In gravelly soils (on old river terraces) and stony soils, the fine material of the upper layer is blown away and a layer of gravel (desert pavement) or boulders remains at the surface, preventing further erosion. Although rain is scarce, it often falls in short heavy showers preceded by a real dust storm. Desert soils, having a thin brittle surface crust, may have a low infiltration rate and consequently there is much sheet, rill and even gully erosion. Much water is discharged through deep, normally dry, valleys. A few annual grasses develop irregularly because rainfall is irregular in amount, period of the year and position.

There is a difference in soil conditions between tropical and subtropical deserts. In the tropics, the short rainy season is always warm; in the subtropics, rain may fall in a cool season. Some rain in a warm season means a short period of tropical soil formation (Ferralic Arenosols, Luvic Xerosols). Some rain in a cool season, when evapotranspiration is rather low, leads to formation of different soils (Calcic and Haplic Xerosols and sometimes Yermosols) and less intense mineralization of organic matter. In continental subtropical deserts and semi-deserts, the A horizon is more developed, particularly if winters are cold.

In semi-deserts, there is more precipitation; the rainy season is somewhat longer than in the deserts. Soil development is more distinct. Soils develop even more in the transition towards the sub-humid zone. It is hardly possible to describe all soils, because there are transitions to regions with a temperate, a Mediterranean, a subtropical, a monsoon and a humid tropical climate; there are therefore various Cambisols, Luvisols and Arenosols, for instance.

In steppe, prairy and pampa landscapes, thick loess deposits can be found. These are aeolian deposits of silt-sized material that is blown to very great heights in the air, carried over long distances and deposited when there is no wind. Loess soils in semi-arid or sub-humid climatic zones often have soils like Kastanozems and Phaeozems, the soils of prairies and pampas. Solonchaks, Solonetz, Regosols, Arenosols, Fluvisols and Gleysols occur too. Luvisols are common in older regions or in areas with somewhat more rapid soil development.

6 The US Soil Taxonomy

6.1 The system

In many countries, systems of soil classification have been developed based on an extensive knowledge of national soils. A comprehensive system of soil classification of all soils of the world did not exist until recently. Soil Survey Staff of the Soil Conservation Service in the United States of America tried to develop such a comprehensive system in consultation with many soil scientists all over the world. After fifteen years of intensive work, the book 'Soil Taxonomy' was published (Soil Survey Staff, 1975). Several preliminary versions of this book have circulated. The system has been tested in many countries. It is the best system so far, although for soils in the tropics, which are less well known, the system needs improvement. French, British and Australian soil scientists have also developed separate systems of soil classification that include soils of the tropics. A Brazilian sy   ᷤ .oncentrates on tropical soils. Most other systems of soil classification such as the Russian and the German ones deal mainly with soils of these countries. Although some subtropical and tropical soils are included.

'Soil Taxonomy' is widely used. In mar important publications, soils are classified according to it. Even an 'introduction' must impart an understanding of at least the main characteristics. They are given here in a simplified way. The original book with all details has 754 pages! It classifies a soil in six categories.

The first category is the *soil order*. There are 10 orders; alphabetically they are Alfisols, Aridisols, Entisols, Histosols, Inceptisols, Mollisols, Oxisols, Spodosols, Ultisols and Vertisols. Some names are similar to those of the major soils of the Soil Map of the World. Histosols and Vertisols include almost the same soils. Alfisols are similar to Luvisols; Aridisols are almost similar to Xerosols and Yermosols; Oxisols to Ferralsols; and Ultisols to Acrisols. However some major soils of the FAO world map are not in the first category of 'Soil Taxonomy', for instance Solonchaks, Andosols, Gleysols, Chernozems and Regosols. Those are distinguished in the second or third category of 'Soil Taxanomy'.

The second category is *suborders*, according to diagnostic soil horizons and properties. Soil horizons and soil properties used to characterize the higher taxa of the classification system are also diagnostic horizons and diagnostic properties. Many of them are similar to those mentioned in Section 4.3 and 4.4. For example, a mollic epipedon (epipedon = surface A horizon) is a mollic A horizon of FAO. There are also umbric, histic and ochric epipedons. For the subsurface horizons ('B horizons' of FAO) there is also similarity, for example the argillic, natric, cambic and oxic horizons. However there are also some differences not mentioned here.

Each suborder consists of a number of *great groups*. These great groups are divided into *subgroups*, which consist of *families;* and each family consists of several *series*. In the literature, most soils are indicated by names in the third category, the great group, and sometimes by subgroup. However in the fifth category, families, soil properties are used that are important for agricultural evaluation e.g. soil depth and soil slope. Series within a soil family are distinguished mainly to facilitate quantitative interpretation of soil behaviour.

The new names in Soil Taxonomy are artificial. They look strange, but they directly connote important characteristics of the soils. The names of the 10 soil orders have already been given. The names of the suborders consist of two syllables. The first connotes something of the diagnostic properties; the second is the formative element from the soil order name. For example an 'Ustert' is a Vertisols (ert from Ve*rt*isol), and 'ust' from ustic soil moisture regime, indicating a prolonged dry season. The name of a great group consists of the name of the suborder and a prefix also suggesting diagnostic properties. A great group in the suborder of Usterts is, for example, Chromustert. The prefix 'chrom' refers to a high chroma (brown soil). The great group 'Chromusterts' of Soil Taxonomy indicates therefore a Vertisol (–ert) with an ustic moisture regime (–ustert) and a high chroma. On the Soil Map of the World, these soils are mapped as 'Chromic Vertisols' and they are not defined by soil moisture regime.

Soil Taxonomy has 10 orders, 47 suborders and 230 great groups, of which some 140 occur in the tropics. About 60 of them are probably important because they have agricultural potential and because they occupy large areas. There are also intergrades between great groups. There are thousands of families and several ten thousands of series. The great groups in Soil Taxonomy may be compared with the 106 soil units in the legend of the Soil Map of the World. Some are similar; some are combined in one unit for the world map; some are quite different.

In Soil Taxonomy, all classification units (taxa) are defined by soil properties, and the characteristic differences between taxa are also indicated by properties or groups of properties. Definitions of all taxa in each category of

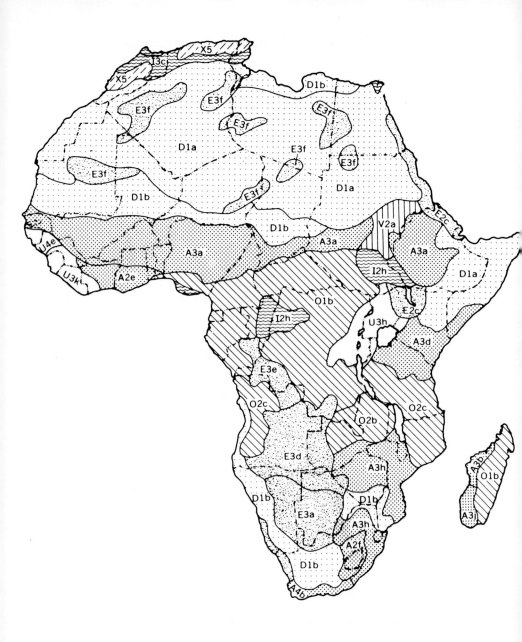

Fig. 6. Soil map of Africa, distribution of orders and principal suborders.

A   Alfisols
A 2e Udalfs with Troporthents
A 3a Ustalfs with Tropepts
A 3b Ustalfs with Troporthents
A 3d Ustalfs with Usterts
A 3f Ustalfs with Ustolls
A 3j Plinthustalfs with Ustorthents
A 4b Xeralfs with Xerorthents

D   Aridisols
D 1a Aridisols with Orthents
D 1b Aridisols with Psamments

E   Entisols
E 2c Torriorthents with Aridisols
E 3a Psamments with Aridisols
E 3d Psamments with Ustalfs
E 3f Psamments (shifting sands)

I   Inceptisols
I 2c   Haplaquepts with Humaquepts
I 2f   Tropaquepts with Hydraquents
I 2h   Tropaquepts with Tropaquents

O   Oxisols
O 1b Orthox with Tropudults
O 2b Ustox with Tropustults
O 2c Ustox with Ustalfs

U   Ultisols
U 3h Tropudults with Orthox
U 3k Tropudults with Tropudalfs
U 4e Tropustults with Ustalfs

V   Vertisols
V 2a Usterts with Tropaquepts

X   Soils in areas with mountains
X 5   Xeric great groups of Alfisols, Entisols, Inceptisols, Mollisols and Ultisols

Source: Soil Map of the World prepared by the Soil Geography Unit of the US Soil Conservation Service, Washington, 1972.

the classification system are quantitative. The boundaries between the taxa are precisely fixed. Such a system is often called a 'morphometric' system of soil classification, because the properties are quantitative. Many properties can only be determined in a laboratory, a disadvantage for direct classification of soils on the spot.

6.2 Soil orders and suborders

A short description of the soil orders and the word-root (in brackets) for the names of suborders and great groups is given below. The comparable units of the Soil Map of the World (SMW) are given as far as possible.

Histosols (–ist)   Organic or peat soils. SMW: Histosols.
Spodosols (–od)   Soils with a spodic horizon. SMW: Podzols.
Oxisols (–ox)   Soils with an oxic horizon. SMW: Ferralsols.
Vertisols (–ert)   Similar to the Vertisols of the Soil Map of the World.
Aridisols (–id)   Usually dry soils, an arid soil moisture regime, with an ochric and sometimes an argillic horizon. SMW: Yermosols and Xerosols.
Ultisols (–ult)   Soil with an argillic horizon and a low base saturation, V < 35%. SMW: Acrisols, and part of Nitosols and Luvisols as far as V < 35%. The difficulty here is that the limit for base saturation is 35% whereas for the units of the SMW it is 50%.
Mollisols (–oll)   Soils with a mollic horizon. SMW: Chernozems, Kastanozems, some Phaeozems.
Alfisols (–alf)   Soils with an argillic horizon and a high base saturation, V > 35%. SMW: Luvisols, Nitosols, Acrisols with V > 35%. See the remark for Ultisols.
Inceptisols (–ept)   Younger soils with a cambic horizon. SMW: Cambisols and Fluvisols.
Entisols (–ent)   Young soils with only an ochric horizon. SMW: Regosols, Arenosols, Fluvisols.

A set of formative elements has been developed in order to distinguish the suborders. The most important ones are listed below.

Alb–   With an albic horizon. SMW: albic E horizon.
And–   In volcanic ash material. SMW: Andosols.
Aqu–   With aquic moisture regimes. SMW: Gleysols and Gleyic soils.
Arg–   Presence of an argillic horizon. SMW: argillic B horizon.
Ferr–   Presence of iron.
Fluv–   In flood plains. SMW: Fluvisols.

80

Hum– Presence of organic matter.
Ochr– With an ochric epipedon. SMW: ochric A horizon.
Orth– The common suborder.
Psamm– With a sand texture. SMW: Arenosols and some Regosols.
Torr– With a torric (aridic) soil moisture regime.
Ud– With a udic moisture regime.
Umbr– With an umbric horizon. SMW: umbric B horizon.
Ust– With an ustic moisture regime.
Xer– With a xeric moisture regime.

With these elements, many names of suborders are made. Some examples are given together with the approximately equivalent unit of the Soil Map of the World.

Andept – Andosol (Plate 4)
Aquept – Gleysol (Pate 3)
Fluvent – Fluvisol (Plate 1)
Orthid – Xerosol and Yermosol (Plate 9).

The names in this list cannot be used in the other direction. A Gleysol is not always an Aquept, because there are many suborders with the element 'aqu–' e.g. Aqualfs, Aquents, Aquolls, Aquox, Aquods, Aquults; they all have hydromorphic properties. Such suborders are shown as Gleysols or Gleyic soils on the Soil Map of the World; however in Soil Taxonomy such soils are distributed over several soil orders. A list of suborders occurring in tropical and subtropical regions is given below. Approximate equivalents of SMW units are given as well.

Alfisols
Aqualfs   Gleyic Luvisols
Udalfs   Orthic Luvisols, Nitosols
Ustalfs   Luvisols (monsoon climate)
Xeralfs   Orthic, Chromic Luvisols

Aridisols
Argids   Luvic Xerosols, Yermosols
Orthids   Xerosols, Yermosols

Entisols
Aquents   Gleysols
Fluvents   Fluvisols
Orthents   Regosols
Psamments   Regosols (sandy)

Histosols

Fibrists	Histosols (rather dry, almost not decomposed)
Folists	Histosols (wet, almost undecomposed)
Hemists	Histosols (partly decomposed)
Saprists	Histosols (decomposed)

Inceptisols

Andepts	Andosols
Aquepts	Gleysols
Ochrepts	Cambisols
Tropepts	Cambisols (in the tropics)
Umbrepts	Humic Cambisols

Mollisols

Aquolls	Mollic Gleysols and Gleyic Phaeozems
Rendolls	Rendzinas
Udolls	Phaeozems
Ustolls	Kastanozems

Oxisols

Aquox	Ferralsols (hydromorphic)
Humox	Humic Ferralsols
Orthox	Orthic and Rhodic Ferralsols
Ustox	Orthic and Rhodic Ferralsols

Spodosols

Aquods	Gleyic Podzols
Ferrods	Ferric Podzols
Humods	Humic Podzols
Orthods	Orthic Podzols

Ultisols

Aquults	Gleyic Acrisols
Humults	Humic Acrisols and Nitosols
Udults	Orthic Acrisols and Nitosols
Ustults	Acrisols (monsoon climate)
Xerults	Acrisols (semi-arid climate)

Vertisols

Torrerts	Vertisols (desert climate)

Uderts	Vertisols (humid climate)
Usterts	Vertisols (monsoon climate)
Xererts	Vertisols (semi-arid climate)

Table 4 gives an idea of the land area of the soil orders, for the world and for the tropics.

Table 4. Land area of different soil orders in millions of hectares.

Soil order	World land area[1]		Land area in the tropics[2]	
	(million ha)	(%)	(million ha)	(%)
Alfisols	1 730	13.1	800	16.2
Aridisols	2 480	18.8	900	18.4
Entisols	1 090	8.2	400	8.2
Histosols	120	0.9	–	–
Inceptisols	1 170	8.9	400	8.3
Mollisols	1 130	8.6	50	1.0
Oxisols	1 120	8.5	1 100	22.5
Spodosols	560	4.3	–	–
Ultisols	730	5.6	550	11.2
Vertisols	230	1.8	100	2.0
Mountains	2 810	21.3	600	12.2
Total	13 170		4 900	

1. Figures of Soil Geography Unit, Soil Conservation Service, Washington, March 1973.
2. Figures of Sanchez (1976), calculated on the basis of a general soil map of the world in: Committee on Tropical Soils (1972).

6.3 Great groups

Another set of formative elements to be used in naming great groups has been developed. The most common ones are listed below.

Acr– Soils with extreme weathering.
Calc– Soils with a calcic horizon.
Camb– Soils with a cambic horizon.
Chrom– Soils with a high chroma.
Dur– Soils with a duripan.
Dystr– Soils with low base saturation.
Eutr– Soils with high base saturation.
Gibbs– Soils with gibbsite.
Gyps– Soils with a gypsic horizon.

Hapl– Soils with minimum horizon development.
Natr– Soils with a natric horizon.
Palae– Soils with an extreme development.
Plinth– Soils with plinthite.
Rhod– Dark red soils.
Sal– Soils with a salic horizon.
Sombr– Soils with a dark horizon.
Sulf– Soils with sulphides.
Trop– Soils in a humid and continually warm climate.
Vitr– Soils in fresh volcanic ash.

Most of the elements mentioned in the foregoing list for naming suborders, are also used for naming great groups.

Some examples of great groups are given together with the approximate equivalent of the unit in the Soil Map of the World.

Plinthustalf An Alfisol with an ustic soil moisture regime and with plinthite. SMW: Plinthitic Luvisol.
Calciorthid An Aridisol of the most common suborder, with a calcic horizon. SMW: Calcic Xerosol. (Plate 9).
Torripsamment An Entisol in sandy material and with an aridic soil moisture regime. SMW: Regosol.
Dystropept An Inceptisol in the tropics with a low base saturation. SMW: Dystric Cambisol. (Plate 15).
Haplohumox An Oxisol with more organic matter than normal but with minimum development. SMW: Humic Ferralsol.
Tropaquod A Spodosol (SMW: Podzol) in the tropics with a high ground-water table. SMW: Gleyic Podzol.
Paleustult An Ultisol with an ustic soil moisture regime and an excessive development. SMW: Ferric Acrisol.

These are selected examples. Many great groups cannot easily be translated into the soil units of the Soil Map of the World. The reverse is not simple either. There are not only two different 'languages' but there is also a difference in definition (for example the limits of base saturation, 35% in Soil Taxonomy and 50% in SMW) and there is a difference in soil properties used to classify soils.

There is much more. This is only a short introduction in order to demonstrate that once a soil is classified according to Soil Taxonomy it is not too difficult to understand its main properties. The soil profiles in this book (Plates 1-16) are indicated by their names according to the Soil Map of the

World. In the short descriptions, the name according to Soil Taxonomy is given as well.

In Volume I, 'Legend' of the Soil Map of the World, reference is made to equivalent soils in various soil classification systems. Soil scientists who would like to know more about Soil Taxonomy might study the book by Buol et al. (1979) that gives a less simplified introduction than has been given here. It also has chapters on soils of each order. This study might be followed by an intensive study of 'Soil Taxonomy' (Soil Survey Staff, 1975), and by exercises in soil classification. There are many examples of soil descriptions in Soil Taxonomy.

Below are the main great groups occurring in the tropics together with the soil unit of the Soil Map of the World into which the soils are mapped.

Great groups (Soil Taxonomy)	*Soil unit* (Soil Map of the World)
Acrohumox	Acric Humic Ferralsols
Acrorthox	Acric Ferralsols
Acrustox	Acric Ferralsols
Albaqualfs	Eutric Planosols
Albaquults	Dystric Planosols
Chromusterts	Chromic Vertisols
Dystrandepts	Ochric Andosols (Plate 4)
Dystropepts	Dystric Cambisols (Plate 15)
Eutrandepts	Mollic Andosols
Eutropepts	Eutric Cambisols
Eutrorthox	Ferralsols
Eutrustox	Ferralsols
Gibbsiaquox	Gleyic Ferralsols
Gibbsihumox	Humic Ferralsols
Gibbsiorthox	Ferralsols
Haplohumox	Humic Ferralsols
Haplorthox	Ferralsols (Plate 7)
Haplustox	Orthic Ferralsols
Humitropepts	Humic Cambisols
Hydrandepts	Humic Andosols
Ochraquox	Gleyic Ferralsols
Pellusterts	Pellic Vertisols
Plinthaqualfs	Plinthic Gleyic Luvisols (Plate 13)
Plinthaquepts	Plinthic Gleysols

Plinthaquox	Plinthic Ferralsols
Plinthaquults	Plinthic Acrisols
Plinthohumults	Plinthic Humic Acrisols
Plinthudults	Plinthic Acrisols
Plinthustalfs	Plinthic Luvisols
Plinthustults	Plinthic Acrisols
Rhodudults	Rhodic Acrisols
Salorthids	Solonchaks (Plate 2)
Sombrihumox	Humic Ferralsols
Sombriorthox	Humic Ferralsols
Sombriustox	Humic Ferralsols
Sulfaquents	Thionic Fluvosols
Sulfaquepts	Thionic Fluvisols
Tropaqualfs	Gleyic Luvisols
Tropaquents	Gleysols
Tropaquepts	Gleysols (Plate 3)
Tropaquods	Gleyic Podzols
Tropaquults	Gleyic Acrisols
Tropohumods	Humic Podzols (Plate 6)
Trophumults	Humic Acrisols and Humic Nitosols
Tropofluvents	Fluvisols
Troporthents	Regosols
Troporthods	Orthic Podzols
Tropopsamments	Arenosols
Tropudalfs	Orthic Luvisols and Eutric Nitosols
Tropudults	Orthic Acrisols and Dystric Nitosols
Umbraquox	Humic Ferralsols
Umbriothox	Humic Ferralsols
Ustifluvents	Fluvisols (Plate 1)
Ustipsamments	Arenosols (Plate 5)
Ustorthents	Regosols
Ustropepts	Cambisols
Vitrandepts	Vitric Andosols

Selected literature: Buol et al. (1979); Soil Survey Staff (1975).

7 Agricultural productivity of soils

Agricultural production depends on conditions of soil and climate. These conditions vary from place to place; therefore their regional distribution has to be studied. Moreover there is another important factor: the farmer. His ability to grow crops and to raise livestock is probably the crucial factor. In almost every situation, the farmer decides what to grow and how to grow crops. Tradition and a long experience as well as socio-economic conditions are important factors in a farmer's decisions. Farming in many regions of the world is rather risky. Nobody knows better than a farmer how much risk he can take. In most systems of traditional farming, risks are minimized. They have to be studied carefully.

One of the main tasks of a soil specialist is to study soils in view of agricultural production. What is the present situation and what is the potential for crops? How can productivity of the various soils be improved? For which crops are those soils most suitable? Can soil conditions be improved? And how much product can be expected? To answer such questions, the type and level of farm management have to be defined as well. This is not only a technical-agricultural matter; economics is often even more important. Every improvement costs more effort and money, and consequently the crop yield must be higher than before in order to get profit. A rule of the thumb is that the profit should be at least two times as much as the extra costs; otherwise farmers are not willing to change their farming system.

A study on soil-crop relationships also implies a good knowledge of crops, because all crops have their preference for particular environmental conditions. Knowledge of plant diseases is important too.

The study of agricultural productivity from a technical point of view is the study of the soil-climate-crop system. It is often found that crop yields are related to some soil properties, e.g. texture, pH, colour, hydromorphic properties, content of organic matter. Such a discovery may be important, however, also for other regions; for other crops, other properties may be more important. In fact single soil properties or a combination of some of them are not important as such. Important is only how these and many other properties influence the growing conditions of crops. Basically these growing conditions of crops are determined by six main regimes:

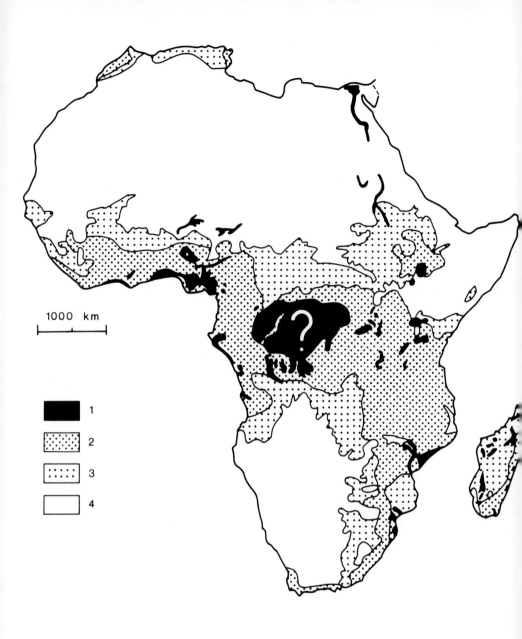

Fig. 7. Generalized map of agricultural potential of Africa.

This map was prepared by the author from information of the FAO/Unesco Soil Map of the World, Volume 6 and various other sources. See also Figures 4, 5 and 6.

Legend
1. Land with high potential (some 50% of the areas indicated belong to this class).
2. Land with moderate potential (some 20 tot 50% of the areas indicated belong to this class).
3. Land with low potential (some 20 to 50% of the areas indicated belong to this class).
4. Land without potential (all land indicated belongs to this class, except a few minor areas belonging to Class 2 or 3).

The map is highly simplified, the scale is small, consequently only large areas are indicated. The large Class 1 area in the central part of Africa was hardly investigated and the classification is uncertain.

Reference is made to FAO (1978 'Report on the Agro-Ecological zones project with results for Africa'. World Soil Res. Rep. 48, Rome), showing small-scale suitability maps for various crops.

the moisture regime
the nutrient regime
the biological regime
the temperature regime
the air regime
the mineral regime.

These regimes are closely interrelated and interdependent, and have to be studied carefully in assessing soils for agricultural production.

Moisture regime

Section 4.5 gives a general classification of soil moisture regimes. In practice, much more has to be known, such as what is the soil moisture regime during the growing season of a crop, how much soil water is available in various growing stages, how much water can be absorbed by the soil to the depth of the rooting system, can the roots reach the capillary zone? Factors and soil properties important for the evaluation of the soil water regime are, for example, rainfall distribution, soil texture, content of organic matter, rooting volume and depth. Deficiencies of soil moisture do occur in three quarters of all tropical soils.

Nutrient regime

The nutrient supply of soils depends on the available nutrients, not only N, P and K, but also Ca, S, Mg, Zn, Mn and many others. The N supply is closely related to the content of organic matter, and to the presence of legumes. Phosphorus is also related to organic matter, and most K is available in the base exchange complex. Presence of weatherable minerals and of toxic ions such as aluminium, and boron also determine the nutrient regime. Deficiences of N, P or K alone or in combination, are common in tropical and subtropical soils. Many soils fix P, and shortage of N is often the main constraint for crop production.

Air regime

The air regime is an important aspect of the soil, because roots need oxygen, and produce carbon dioxide, which has to escape to the air. Penetration of oxygen and diffusion of carbon dioxide decrease with soil depth. The total volume of all pores and the type of pores in the rootable zone influence the growth of the roots and consequently the crop yield.

Temperature regime

A general classification has already been given in Section 4.5 Various crops have an upper and a lower temperature during growth stages not only of the air but also of the soil. For example soil temperature < 20 °C and > 33 °C influence the gross photosynthesis of rice. In arid regions, the temperature of the surface soil can rise to more than 60 °C.

Biological regime

The activity of all macro and micro flora and fauna in a soil determines the biological regime. Per gram of soil, there are some millions of bacteria, fungi, actomycetes, algae and protozoa. The living biological mass in a surface soil to a depth of 20 cm is from 200 to more than 1000 kg.ha^{-1}. At a depth of some 40 cm, this mass is some 30% and at a depth of some 70 cm about 10% of that of the surface soil. There are great variations. Decomposition of dead organic material, release of nitrogen, buffering of nutrients and many other processes are significant. Biological activity can be stimulated, for instance, by application of organic manure or compost. Macro-organisms like worms and termites eat and thoroughly mix mineral and organic material (homogenization). For optimum biological activity, specific soil moisture, temperature and air regimes are required. In dry soils, biological activity is very low.

Mineral regime

As already stated, the presence of weatherable minerals, their type and amount, as well as the type and amount of clay minerals are important, not only for the amount of available plant nutrients but also as far as the clay complex is concerned for the cation-exchange processes. The low exchange capacity of kaolinitic clays, characteristic for many tropical soils, often limits crop production.

The above soil regimes are the real factors influencing crop production. These regimes depend closely on various chemical, physical, biological and mineralogical properties, which should therefore be studied in detail to determine their influence on the various regimes. The regimes are the keys to agricultural evaluation, to assess potentialities and to decide on possible measures for land improvement.

It seems strange that there is hardly any relation to the classification of major soils, but in reality it is not strange at all. The classification of major soils is based on soil properties in order to distinguish the various soils. It is done in such a way that they can be shown on a map, showing the occurrence and regional distribution of soils. On small scale soil maps, particularly on the very small scale of the Soil Map of the World (1 to 5 million) only a few major soil properties are considered. For agricultural evaluation, other soil properties have to be studied too.

The natural biological production in the humid tropics is very high, e.g. the annual dry matter production of tropical rain forest is estimated at 28 t.ha^{-1}, for a swamp it is 20 t.ha^{-1} and for tropical grassland some 8 t.ha^{-1}. In the arid regions, it is of course much lower. Natural grazing land in the Sahel has a dry matter production of about 2 t.ha^{-1}.

In most tropical countries crop yields are low, mainly because of the rather poor farm management (traditional farming). There are examples of improved farming with crop yields 3 to 8 times as high as those of traditional farming. During the last decade, progress has been made in determining the appropriate level of farm management. The conclusion of all specialists is that crop yields can be tremendously increased if farm management is improved. At this stage, solar energy also plays a role, because in the humid tropics the sky is cloudy for much of the day. In the arid tropics, solar energy is more abundant, but precipitation is low and soil moisture is the main constraint. This, however, is not always true since in semi-arid regions nitrogen and phosphorus might be the main constraints, so that available soil moisture is not limiting.

Soils in many tropical countries have a potential for agricultural production, particularly in Latin America, Africa, and in some parts of Asia. However, general improvement of agricultural production is time-consuming, and has to be performed step by step. Often it first needs a change in socio-economic conditions, particularly of the rural population.

8 Soil erosion: destruction of land

Soil erosion is extensively dealt with in many books and articles, because of its importance in the tropics. Both water and wind erosion have damaged much productive land. Most severe soil erosion is caused by burning and cutting forest on sloping land in the humid tropics, and by overgrazing of the natural grassland regions with prolonged dry seasons. The increasing population needs more firewood. Wood is cut for pulping or timber, and is exported by many countries where virgin forests still occur. As productivity of much land is very low and agricultural production still continues on a traditional level of farming, more land is needed to get more food. Spontaneous reclamation of forest land is 75% of all land reclamation in the world. Much steep sloping land is reclaimed without terracing and consequently soil erosion increases very rapidly in many countries. In regions with long dry seasons, where trees are already scarce, many trees are cut for firewood. In the tropics 80% of all woodcutting is for firewood.

All these problems are increasing: soil erosion, deforestation, overgrazing, wind erosion and desertification. Specialists know various methods of soil conservation, but little is done. Even in some rich countries, soil erosion continues to increase despite various conservation projects. A study of these world problems indicates that the major reasons are socio-economic and often mainly political. A small farmer in miserable conditions cannot be blamed for damaging vegetation and soils if he tries to get a minimum of food for his family. Fortunately several scientists have already concluded that a poor small farmer often gets better crops and higher yields per hectare than richer neighbours. It is worse that land of rather rich farmers and even of corporations and of agribusiness firms is eroding too.

Sheet erosion is a type of soil erosion that does not get enough attention. Every year a very thin layer of the surface soil is eroded. It is a slow, but an almost continuous process of damaging land. It occurs on very extensive areas and the final result can be observed only after some decades.

Reforestation and forest plantation for timber and pulp in the tropics is only done on a small scale. Foresters expect serious problems within a few decades. More than 30% of the present forest area is inaccessible or it has to be protected in order to regulate hydrology. Eroded soil material is deposited in lower-lying areas, in valleys and deltas often damaging that land too. Water reservoirs behind dams and various lakes are filled with sediments. In many river basins the hydrological balance is disturbed. During the rainy season, the river discharges are abnormally high. Disastrous floods have already damaged much land. As deforestation and soil erosion increase, more disasters can be expected.

Much more can be written; many examples can be given; the problem of soil salinization, particularly important in irrigation projects in semi-arid and arid regions, could be discussed too. It is too much for an introduction. Moreover there are several special books and articles dealing with these and other problems of land deterioration. These problems are relevant to all mankind, not just to soil specialists or soil conservationists.

Another, perhaps greater problem is more difficult to solve: the expanding non-agricultural use of land. The world's population is increasing by 80 million per annum. Within 35 years it will have doubled. Instead of 4000 million there will be 8000 million in 2015. They will need houses and roads. Industry will expand; highways will be constructed. Most people live in areas where the soils are best for agriculture. Every year, much land that has been used for centuries to produce food is turned over to other uses. Worldwide the decrease in cultivated land is about 0.2 to 0.5% per year, which means that 3 to 7 million hectares of cultivated land are lost to other uses. People indeed need houses, industries and roads but it is doubtful whether the best land need be used for these purposes.

Most people do not have any idea about soil erosion, salinization, desertification or loss to other uses. It seems more effective to survey and to demonstrate on maps the extent and severity of the various problems for a certain region or country than to discuss these problems without data.

9   Soil improvement

9.1   Fertilizers

The major limiting factor in crop production is often available nutrients in soils. Without adding stable manure or fertilizers, crop production depends on the amounts of nutrients released by soil and added by rainwater and dust (total not more than 10 or 30 kg.ha^{-1} of N, P and K; it may be higher in some rich volcanic soils, and in paddy soils with green-blue algae). In soils with leguminous weeds, some extra N can be added by N fixation. In most soils, N and P are always at a minimum. In older tropical soils, the amount of weatherable minerals, which can supply necessary nutrients, is little, if any. Often the content of organic matter and the CEC are low too. Moreover many soils have a low to very low base saturation, or soluble aluminium, soluble salts or Na$^+$ make the soil toxic. Fixation of P is normal in many tropical soils, because of the presence of iron compounds that easily fix P.

The nutrient status of soils can be improved by adding natural fertilizers (manure, compost, ash), and chemical fertilizers. The advantages of organic fertilizers are increase in organic matter, biological activity and nutrient supply. The content of nutrients in organic fertilizers, however, is rather low. Various experiments have clearly shown that it is necessary for every farmer to collect and preserve as much manure and compost as possible and to add this to his soils. In combination with weeding, it can increase low crop yields by 50% or more.

The next step might be application of chemical fertilizers, particularly N, P and K. If pH and V are low, some lime has to be added first. If there is aluminium toxicity, lime has to be mixed with the soil, because crop roots do not penetrate in an aluminium-rich soil. Most tropical soils with a pH lower than 5 contain soluble aluminium. Aluminium-toxicity is more severe in Latin America than in Africa, because in Africa almost all soils are influenced by calcareous dust from the deserts. In many clayey soils, potassium is not always needed initially. Sulphur (S) is also an element that often has to be added, because in the humid tropics it is leached from older soils. This also applies to various minor elements. Sulphur is present in some commercial fertilizers; most minor elements are not. The latter may be available in compost.

The problem of soil fertility and the application of fertilizers is too wide to discuss here. Sanchez (1976) pays much attention to it. Some remarks need to be made. The first is on the use of chemical analysis of soil samples as a basis for advice on the type and amount of fertilizers to be given. Soil can be analyzed by various methods. Results are often different. The interpretation of the data is difficult, because it has to be based on results of fertilizer experiments in the field. Since the contents of P and K in soil samples are mostly very low and because N is always needed, it can generally be said that NPK fertilizers are necessary. In order to have at least a general impression of how to interpret results of soil analysis, the following data are given. If available P is less than 5 ppm, it is very low; if it is more than 30 ppm, it is rather high. If available K is less than 40 ppm, it is very low and, if it is more than 150 ppm, it is high. More difficult to determine is which other elements also need to be given. Often the effect of NPK fertilizers is less than expected, because lime or other elements (Zn, Cu, Mn, B) have to be given too. Instead of soil analysis, foliar analysis can be a great help.

In western Europe the advice on fertilizer application is based on soil and foliar analysis in combination with various fertilizer experiments in the field on the main soils and with various crops, because each crop has a specific need for nutrients. It takes many years to collect sufficient data. In the tropics, plant nutrients are even more difficult to assess, not only because soil conditions are less known, but even more because of the typical behaviour of most tropical soils. Another problem is that most research on the application of fertilizers in tropical countries is done for commercial crops that often grow on the better soils, whereas the important food crops get less attention.

The second point to be discussed gives a somewhat more optimistic view, because it is well known that almost all cultivated soils need manure and fertilizers in order to increase crop yields. It is not necessary to tripple or quadruple yields in a few years and therefore simple field trials can be set up, demonstration fields can be set out and within a few years farmers can be advised what to do. With rather small amounts of fertilizers, much can be gained. As soon as some progress is made with the application of fertilizers, other problems have to be solved, for instance of plant protection or plant breeding. Local crop varieties react to fertilizers to a certain extent; however, as soon as the nutrient status of soils is improved, new crop varieties are needed that react better to fertilizers. Therefore the first applications of chemical fertilizers are not meant to get high yields, but to increase crop yields under local conditions by 25 or 50%. This is not too difficult, at least when socioeconomic conditions are favourable and extra profits are for the farmers. For cereal grain crops, that produce about 75% of all food, one ton of fertilizer (expressed as N, P_2O_5 or K_2O) produces in average 10 tons of grain. In most tropical countries, it is even more.

The optimistic views of specialists on crop potentials in the tropics are based on knowledge and experience with various types of fertilizers and manure, and on better knowledge of soil conditions. It is true that many soils have other properties limiting crop production, such as an indurated iron pan, plinthite, shallow depth, steep slopes or surface crusts. Fortunately there are enough soils with good physical soil conditions and without such limiting properties, and those need fertilizers.

A low soil fertility is not only a problem of tropical or subtropical soils. Almost any soil needs fertilizers if high yields are wanted. In 1975, some 82 million tons of NPK fertilizers (calculated as N, P_2O_5 and K_2O) were applied throughout the world. Approximately 30% of it was used on cereal cropland (1000 million ha), 19% on other food cropland (400 million ha), 20% on non-food cropland (100 million ha), and 31% on grassland (3 044 million ha). It is calculated that of all cereal cropland only 20% gets fertilizers, and of the world's grassland only 3% gets fertilizers. The annual increase in fertilizer use is some 7%. A much higher increase may be expected in the near future. Europe uses 34% of all fertilizers, North and Central America 23%, Latin America 3%, Africa 3%, Asia 19%, Oceania 2% and the Soviet Union 17%.

If the nutrient status of the tropical soils currently cultivated is improved by adding appropriate fertilizers, it could be much less necessary to reclaim and cultivate new land.

Selected literature: Aubert and Pinta (1977); Bolt (1978); FAO (1973a); Finck (1963); de Geus (1973); Kapagé (1976); Kawaguchi and Kyuma (1977); Mengel and Kirkley (1978); Sanchez (1973; 1976); Young (1976).

9.2 Irrigation

Moisture stress is probably, the second problem in many soils. Good land in the tropics can produce two or three crops per year, if there is enough water. This is impossible if there is a dry season. The length and intensity of the dry season determine the potential for crops. In northerly climates, winters are too cold, and solar radiation is too low to grow crops, and so in the open field only one crop can be grown. In parts of the tropics, however, temperature and solar radiation are favourable, only water is lacking. In fact, the situations are similar: something is lacking. Since it is easier to get water if rivers are near by or if deep groundwater can be pumped to the surface, irrigation allows more crops. In many regions, only supplementary irrigation is needed. In arid regions, irrigation induces soil salinization, because rainfall is too low to leach soluble salts during the rainy season and consequently salts accumulate in soils, which gradually become saline (Section 3.5).

The total area of irrigated land on the world is 210 million hectares. It seems that the maximum area that could be irrigated is about 450 million hectares, of which 300 million are in Asia. In the tropics, most irrigated land is used to grow rice (paddy). In some regions, irrigation water can be controlled; in other regions land is flooded during high discharge of rivers in the rainy season.

Irrigation influences soil conditions. In permanently flooded fields, reduction processes predominate and iron and manganese become soluble to some degree. Translocation followed by immobilization of these compounds during dry periods, when air can penetrate the upper layers of soil, causes the formation of horizons of iron and manganese accumulation (Plate 16). Moreover the cultivation of rice fields under flooded conditions favours the formation of less permeable plough layers. Irrigation water in volcanic regions brings valuable nutrients to the fields, many rivers carry a silt load. This material is sedimented on irrigated land, adding fresh material to the soil, forming a layer of sediment. According to the duration and type of irrigation and on the amount of silt carried by the irrigation water, new surface layers are formed some decimetres or sometimes several metres thick.

In all irrigated areas, three factors are important: land levelling, control of irrigation water and the quality of the irrigation water. Land levelling needs constant attention in order to ensure that all parts of an irrigation field get a similar volume of water. This volume should be controlled, although this is often impossible if the discharge of a river cannot be controlled. In many irrigated areas, both land levelling and control of irrigation water can be improved considerably. In irrigated rice fields, water management is often more important than soil conditions. It is difficult, usually impossible, to influence the quality of irrigation water. Quality of irrigation water is important in regions where salinization occurs or is liable. As discussed in Section 3.5 for saline soils, the salt concentration of irrigation water can be derived from conductivity. As this conductivity is much lower than in an extract of a saturated soil, the result is expressed in micro-mho's. Irrigation water with an electrical conductivity (EC) of 750 μmho's or less is considered to be of good quality, if the sodium adsorption ratio (SAR) < 18. An EC of 2000 μmho is very high. Classification of the quality of irrigation water is much more complicated, because the chemical composition of salts, the soil conditions and climate, and farm management are important factors too.

Selected literature: Ayers and Westcot (1976); FAO (1970b); FAO/Unesco (1973); Richards (1954).

9.3 Drainage

Many soils with too high a groundwater and so with hydromorphic properties can be improved by drainage. The groundwater can be lowered by digging open drain ditches or by underground pipes. Such pipes are made of clay, concrete or plastic. The depth needed for the drains and the distance between the drains in a field depend, for instance, on the permeability and drainability of the soils, on the depth to which the groundwater level must be lowered and on precipitation. For more details, reference is made to handbooks on soil drainage. Drainage of saline land is a special subject, because the groundwater has to be lowered to a great depth and the drainage system also serves to carry off the extra water used to dissolve the soluble salts present in the soil. As groundwater in saline regions is mostly highly saline, one must always try to lower the groundwater to such a depth that the capillary zone does not reach the rooting zone of crops.

Selected literature: FAO/Unesco (1973); Richards (1954).

9.4 Management of soils

Most farmers know quite well how to manage their soils, but, as soon as improvements are introduced, management has to be adapted, particularly when machines are introduced. It is impossible to refer to all soils, but only to make some remarks. A cultivated soil is exposed to direct radiation of the sun. Temperature and moisture conditions of soils, particularly of surface soils, change continuously. Heavy showers pour down on a barren soil. Soil under natural conditions in the humid tropics are under forest and not exposed to direct sunshine; the soil surface is covered by a layer of decomposing organic matter; and rain is caught by the vegetation. Fluctuations in temperature and moisture are rather small. The best type of management is to create a situation similar to natural conditions. This, however, is not always possible, except for some perennial crops such as rubber (Hevea), coffee and cocoa. Food crops are annuals, that cover soils for some months only. Sometimes more than one crop can be grown each year and soils are covered for a longer period. Intercropping and mixed cropping may have a similar effect. The best solution is to avoid the direct exposure of soils to sunshine and rain, for example by covering soils with a mulch of non-edible parts of crops, or to have a mixture of various types of crops on the same field, a practice common in traditional farming.

In areas with a long dry season, the surface soil of cultivated land is often hard or crusty, and it is difficult to prepare a seed bed. The introduction of modern (Western) equipment is not always an advantage, because soil structure and porosity are often damaged. It is worthwhile to study the effect of locally used old tools. Machines might have an advantage particularly if work can be done in a short period, various soils being workable only for some days. Conservation of as much rainwater as possible is extremely important in regions with a short rainy season (semi-arid and semi-humid regions).

Selected literature: Bornemiza and Alvarado (1975); Greenland et al. (1977); Papendick et al. (1976); Sanchez (1976); Wambeeke (1974).

9.5 Soil conservation

In order to avoid or to minimize soil erosion, several measures can be taken, including contour ploughing, terracing, and covering soils with a vegetation or a mulch. Methods of soil conservation, including those to minimize wind erosion (wind breaks), and of preventing soil salinity (drainage), are well known and extensively described in handbooks. The problem of a farmer is that introducing soil conservation and the maintenance of it cost money, whereas income hardly increases. Therefore the government has to help. More to the point is that a single farmer can hardly succeed, if his neighbours do not cooperate. Mostly soil conservation has to be done for a whole region (the catchment area of a river or one of its tributaries). Reforestation in the upper part of the basin is often imperative. Here the government has to organize and to direct the conservation project.

A similar situation exists in most irrigation and drainage projects. A single farmer can do little. If his land is near a river or a well, he can irrigate but if water has to be taken a long distance, he needs cooperation. For soil drainage, this is always necessary.

Selected literature: FAO (1976b); Greenland et al. (1977).

9.6 Land reclamation

The ever increasing population, loss of land to other uses, and land misuse force farmers to reclaim new land for cultivation. Land reclamation has been done as long as people cultivate land. During recent decades, the area of newly reclaimed land has increased more than ever before. The total land area that is reclaimed annually from forest is estimated at 5 to 10 million hectares, of which most is spontaneous reclamation, done by farmers without any government plan. A farmer, who needs more land, cannot migrate over a large distance in order to start again. He tries to find suitable land nearby. Therefore much marginal land is reclaimed, although better land may be available somewhere else. An individual farmer can only reclaim a small area. As soon as environmental conditions are such that reclamation has to be done by groups of farmers, the government has to help, for instance by reclamation of coastal areas, swamps and lakes, and by building dykes to protect land from flooding.

Land reclamation in projects is seldom a real succes. Many technical, economic and social mistakes are made. The main reasons for this are unsufficient knowledge and experience, unsufficient investigations to plan a project, poor planning and execution, shortage of money and time, and poor cooperation between agronomists, soil specialists, irrigation and drainage engineers, land-use and settlement planners and farmers. It is incredible that many projects are still started without initial soil survey. For soil survey the main problems are insufficient time (because the government wants to start as soon as possible), detailed investigations are not made even of sample areas, and no real land classification and evaluation are made before planning starts. Most mistakes could be avoided. No reclamation project should start before a pilot project indicates that reclamation could succeed.

Selected literature: Takes (1975).

10 Land evaluation

Land can be evaluated for several purposes, including suitability for food crops or commercial crops, for land taxation, for construction of highways, for land-use planning and for reclamation. Even land evaluation for agricultural purposes is often quite different. All land evaluations are associated with a change in land use. Land evaluation for agriculture means also an investigation of potentials, which includes not only an evaluation of the suitability of land for specific crops or groups of crops (crop rotation) but also of potentials for various systems of farm management, including potential yields, and costs and benefits of farming.

In an area with traditional farming, crops are grown mainly for food and yields are much lower than what is possible. The main constraint is mostly soil fertility. As this is very low, yields of all land are almost the same, often within 10% of the maximum, and within 25% of that with improved farming. As soon as the fertility problems are solved, other factors limit crop production. With fertilizers and manure, crop yields may be doubled and are now 20% of the maximum. The next step may be different for various soils, because at one place a hardpan at a shallow depth may limit rooting of crops, whereas elsewhere soils may be too dry during a part of the growing season or some minor elements may be missing. If such limiting factors can be improved, crops can grow better and yields may increase to 30% of the potential. At the next stage of improvement other limiting factors come into play, and so on. Problems become more and more complicated if the standard of agricultural production gradually becomes higher. More soil investigations (this refers to almost any type of evaluation), and more detailed studies are needed. Land evaluation becomes more complicated. The example also demonstrates that the number of factors involved in evaluation increases and that for each evaluation the purpose of the evaluation should be quite clear. Moreover the investigator must know what the level of farm management is and what it might become in the near future. The main problems of the farmers are the investment in relation to the increasing production, and the increasing risk.

Everywhere environmental conditions are different and often the purpose of land evaluation is different as well. Consequently there can be no universal method of land evaluation. Even a national system of land evaluation or classification is hardly possible, except for a specific purpose, for instance a system of land classification for irrigated farming. Very general classifications on a small scale for a whole country can be made according to a special system. However, for most land development projects this is impossible.

Another complication is that soil conditions are only one of the various factors to be taken into account when evaluating and classifying land. Others factors are, for example topography, hydrology, agronomy, economic and social conditions. Therefore land evaluation is always carried out by a group of specialists. The main tasks of soil specialists are to determine which parts of the region are unsuitable for the purpose of evaluation, and to indicate classes for the rest of the region. Results have to be presented on maps and in reports in such a way that other kinds of scientist can understand limitations and potentials. The ideal solution for soil conditions cannot usually be obtained, and the final result is a compromise. Soil specialists should understand that other disciplines also work with limiting factors.

Evaluating land for taxation is complicated. The soil scientist can indicate suitability and production capacity for the most common crops in the present situation, including the present general level of farm management. Such an evaluation has to be made in cooperation with agronomists and some farmers who know the area.

In some countries of Europe, that have a centrally planned economy, a rather detailed land evaluation and classification are made for crop production. It forces farmers to produce an amount of food that is determined in advance with the help of land classification maps, that show the potential productivity. Such a procedure is wrong because only with trials over many years under normal farming conditions can one predict crop yields, and the various risks cannot be predicted, because nature is capricious.

During recent years, attempts have been made to develop evaluation and classification systems with computers, in order to facilitate handling of as many factors and data as possible. Results seem promising. One may doubt whether the procedures will be a success, because the result does not depend on the computer but on the information used and on the weight given to the data collected.

Selected literature: FAO (1976c).

11 Soil investigations in the tropics

Soil science is young and in the tropics very young. It is also a complicated science because of the many aspects. In many countries of the tropics, a small group of young and enthusiastic soil specialists has started work. They have an important and difficult task.

It is wrong to believe that work is needed on all soils in a few years, and it is also wrong to think that a lot of research work has to be done first. Sometimes research work is done in a similar way and for similar scientific purposes to those in rich countries, where soils have been studied for 80 or 100 years or more. Much attention is often directed to developing and proving theories on soil genesis, and to learning about the various processes that govern the behaviour of soils. Soil classification has been a much discussed problem in the advanced countries during the last decades. This gives the impression that soil classification would be an important problem in tropical countries as well. This impression is supported by the façt that it is the speciality of most soil scientists of the Northern Hemisphere who work in the tropics. One also gets the impression that only laboratories with the most advanced equipment can solve problems. A new topic is the soil data bank, a collection of information on soils that can be handled by a computer.

Soil scientists in tropical countries should beware. It is not necessary and probably even wrong to imitate or compete with advanced specialized research work done in temperate regions. In temperate regions, soil research started in a simple way to solve practical problems. Since those soil scientists succeeded and other specialists could join in, the work has expanded and some of them could concentrate on research. This is particularly done in universities and some specialized research institutes. Most literature and nicely printed reports and soil maps are the result of that type of work. They give a wrong impression about what is going on and what has to be done, because work for practical purposes is mostly done by other specialists, special agencies and consulting firms that do not have time and money to publish all results. Their work is reported in special reports, of which only a few copies are circulated.

Young soil scientists might also become nervous if they discover that about 8 000 articles, reports and books are published annually and abstracted in *Soils and Fertilizers*. Some years ago, the then Director of the Bureau producing those abstracts stated that most of the publications were nothing more than a repetition of what was already known; real important new developments are few.

The best thing for a young group of specialists in a tropical country is probably to start soil research in the field and in the laboratory in a rather simple way. As soil science is mostly applied to agricultural problems and agricultural development, field surveys should be done first. Detailed research is needed to solve particular problems. More general research is done in order to show where similar problems occur or may be expected. Aerial photographs and mozaics are an important tool for all types of soil survey. Much can be learned from farmers experiences and from studies of soil-crop relationships. Cooperation with colleagues of other disciplines is profitable. The nutrient status and the need to apply fertilizers have to be studied from the beginning. Fertilizer trials need to be laid out. Investigations should be concentrated on soils having some potentials. Initially there is no need to study in detail poor soils without potential or soils with typical characteristics that occur only in minor areas. It is important to eliminate as soon as possible all areas with soils that have little or no potential, being thus irrelevant for the purpose of an investigation. By doing so, more than half or three quarters of a project area can often be eliminated at an early stage and more attention can be given to the real work in the better part of the area.

It is necessary to exploit existing knowledge. Therefore existing methods of soil investigation for field and laboratory work must be adapted, possibly to local conditions.

There is no need for a complete data bank. It is probably much better to collect data of the main soils, including profile and landscape photographs, and some soil monoliths. These collections can be used for reference, comparison, classification, demonstration and teaching. Within a few years, such a collection of the main soils becomes valuable. It becomes the nucleus of a soil data bank.

Each government is interested in having a soil map of the whole country. Making such a map takes many years and much effort. Such a map can also be made in various stages. A very simple soil map on a very small scale can be made without much work. If all soil specialists, who travel in various parts of a country do some observation during their trips, and cooperate in such a project the national soil map can be gradually improved. Satellite images can help to delineate the main landscape types. If more is known, a somewhat larger-scale map can be made. The advantage of this procedure is that knowledge of soils increases, on the one hand by doing more detailed work and on the other hand by general exploration.

Time is always short in soil investigations. However it is a big mistake to report data too late. It is much better to investigate and to map soils in a more general way, including some sample areas in more detail and to report the results on time than to be late; otherwise specialists and planners who need the information will continue with their plans and ignore information on soils and soil conditions.

Glossary of older soil names

This glossary provides a selection of names of soils in English that have been used, and are sometimes still used in books and articles. They belong to various soil classification systems.

Each name below is followed by the name of the approximate major soil as used on the Soil Map of the World and explained in this book. Definitions of soils, even if they have a similar name, are sometimes different. Some soils belong to more than one group, but only one of them is mentioned. The only purpose of this glossary is to present a general indication, so that the reader gets at least some idea about these soils if studying publications in which other names are used.

Acid sulphate soils	Thionic Fluvisols
Alkali soils	Solonetz and soils with sodic phase
Alluvial soils	Fluvisols
Ando soils	Andosols
Areno Latosols	Ferralic Arenosols
Arenoferrals	Ferric Arenosols
Argilliluvic soils	Luvisols
Aridic soils	Xerosols and Yermosols
Black earths	Pellic Vertisols
Black earths	Chernozems
Black cotton soils	Vertisols
Black tropical soils	Pellic Vertisols
Bog soils	Histosols
Brown calcimorphic soils	Calcic Xerosols
Brown calcimorphic soils	Calcic Luvisols
Brown Latosols	Orthic Ferralsols
Brown Mediterranian soils	Orthic Luvisols
Brown soils	Calcic Cambisols
Brown soils	Calcic Xerosols
Brown tropical soils	Humic Andosols
Brunizems	Phaeozems
Calcareous soils	Calcic Xerosols

107

Calcisols	Calcic Cambisols
Calcisols	Calcic Xerosols
Cat-clay soils	Thionic Fluvisols
Chestnut soils	Kastanozems
Cinnamon soils	Chromic Cambisols
Cinnamon soils	Chromic Luvisols
Dark Red Latosols	Orthic and Acric Ferralsols
Desert soils	Yermosols and Xerosols
Earthy Latosols	Orthic Ferralsols
Eutrophic Brown soils	Eutric Nitosols
Ferralitic soils	Ferralsols
Ferralitic soils	Ferric Acrisols
Ferrisols	Dystric Nitosols
Ferruginous soils	Ferric Luvisols
Ferruginous soils	Ferralic Cambisols
Fersiallitic soils	Acrisols
Gray-Brown Desert soils	Calcic Xerosols
Gray Desert soils	Yermosols
Gray Desert soils	Xerosols
Gray Podzolic soils	Ferric and Plinthic Luvisols
Gray Wooded soils	Orthic Luvisols
Groundwater Laterites	Plinthic Acrisols
Groundwater Laterites	Plinthic Luvisols
Groundwater Podzol soils	Gleyic Podzols
Grumusols	Vertisols
Halomorphic soils	Solonchaks and Solonetz
Humic Allophane soils	Andosols
Humic Ferralitic soils	Humic Ferralsols
Humic Ferrisols	Humic Nitosols
Humic Ferruginous Latosols	Humic Acrisols
Humic Gley soils	Gleysols
Humic Gley soils	Gleyic Acrisols
Humic Latosols	Humic Ferralsols and Acrisols
Humic Latosols	Humic Nitosols
Hydro Latosols	Gleyic Ferralsols
Hydro Latosols	Gleyic Acrisols
Hydrol Humic Latosols	Humic Andosols
Hydromorphic soils	Gleysols and Gleyic soils
Hydrosols	Gleysols and Gleyic soils
Immature soils	Regosols

Kaolisols	Ferralsols
Kraznozems	Dystric Nitosols
Laterite	Ironstone and ironstone hardpan
Laterite soils	Plinthic Acrisols
Lateritic soils	Ferralsols
Lateritic soils	Acrisols
Latosolic Regosols	Ferralic Arenosols
Latosols	Ferralsols
Latosols	Nitosols
Latosols	Acrisols
Lithomorphic soils	Rendzinas
Lithomorphic soils	Soils with lithic phase
Low Humic Gleysols	Gleysols
Low Humic Latosols	Ferralic Cambisols
Margalitic soils	Vertisols
Meadow soils	Gleysols
Muck soils	Histosols
Ochrosols	Ferralsols
Organic soils	Histosols
Pale Yellow Latosols	Xanthic Ferralsols
Pallid soils	Plinthic Luvisols
Pallid soils	Albic Arenosols
Peat soils	Histosols
Podzol soils	Podzols
Podzolic soils	Luvisols
Prairie soils	Kastanozems
Prairie soils	Phaeozems
Psammentic Latosols	Ferralic Arenosols
Red Desert soils	Luvic Xerosols
Red Earths	Rhodic Ferralsols
Red Latosols	Rhodic Ferralsols
Red Mediterranean soils	Chromic Luvisols
Red Sands	Ferralic Arenosols
Red Podzolic soils	Orthic Acrisols
Red Yellow Latosols	Orthic Ferralsols
Red Yellow Podzolic soils	Ferric and Orthic Acrisols
Red Yellow Podzolic soils	Dystric Nitosols
Reddish-Brown Lateritic soils	Nitosols
Reddish-Brown Lateritic soils	Humic Acrisols
Reddish-Brown Latosols	Nitosols

109

Reddish-Brown soils	Calcic Luvisols
Reddish-Brown soils	Calcic Cambisols
Reddish Prairie soils	Luvic Kastanozems
Rhegosols	Regosols
Rubrozems	Humic Acrisols
Semi-Desert soils	Xerosols
Semi-Desert soils	Calcic Cambisols
Sierozems	Luvic Xerosols
Solodized Solonetz	Solodic Planosols
Solods (Soloths)	Solodic Planosols
Solonchak soils	Solonchaks
Solonetz soils	Solonetz
Steppic soils	Chernozems
Steppic soils	Kastanozems
Terra Rossa	Chromic Luvisols
Terra Roxa Estruturada	Eutric Nitosols and Luvisols
Terra Roxa Ligitima	Rhodic Ferralsols
Tropical Podzols	Humic Podzols
Volcanic soils	Andosols
Volcanic ash soils	Andosols
White sands	Albic Arenosols
Yellow Latosols	Xanthic Ferralsols
Yeltozems	Orthic Acrisols
Zeltozems	Orthic Luvisols, Acrisols

Short description of the soil profiles

Plates 1-16 show typical profiles of various tropical and subtropical soils. Soil depth is indicated in centimetres. Two names are given:

FAO: referring to the name of the FAO/Unesco Soil Map of the World (FAO/Unesco, 1971-1978).

ST: referring to Soil Taxonomy (Soil Survey Staff, 1975) of the Soil Conservation Service of the US Department of Agriculture (Section 6.3).

Soil characteristics that can be seen in the pictures are indicated. Some general information on agricultural evaluation is added.

Plate 1.   FAO: Dystric Fluvisol
ST: Typic Ustifluvent
Site Puricaure, northern Venezuela.
Soil characteristics   Section 3.4. The soil is stratified, consisting of several layers of recent river deposits, mainly loamy and clayey material. There is hardly any horizon development. Roots penetrate to a depth of 50 cm.
Agricultural evaluation   At present poor grazing land. There is low rainfall and a long dry season. The soil is suitable for many crops if it can be irrigated.

Plate 2.   FAO: Orthic Solonchak
ST: Typic Solorthid
Site Mesopotamian Plain, Iraq.
Soil characteristics   Section 3.5. The profile is a two-metre deep wall of a newly constructed main drain. The soil consists of Tigris and Euphrates sediments, and is very saline because of capillary rise of highly saline groundwater. In the layer 0-60 cm the main salt is sodium sulphate; 60-70 cm (dark brown) and 70-140 cm (lighter brown), calcium and magnesium chloride; and 140-210 cm (white) sodium chloride.
Agricultural evaluation   At present very poor, because of extreme salinity. If this soil is well drained and the soluble salts are washed out, it is an excellent soil for irrigated agriculture. With modern farm management, it has high agricultural potential.

Plate 3. FAO: Eutric Gleysol
ST: Typic Tropaquept
Site Marine coastal plain, Surinam.
Soil characteristics Section 3.6. The upper 7 cm consist of organic material. The upper part of the mineral soil (0-19 cm) is an ochric A horizon of clay with a high content of organic matter. The whole soil, particularly the subsoil, is characterized by hydromorphic properties. These are distinct yellowish-red mottles (oxidation), and in the lower part also bluish-gray mottles (reduction). The profile is in an experimental field with artificial drainage (bananas in Polder Santo). Groundwater level varies from 10 to 150 cm. Roots penetrate to a depth of 60 cm.
Agricultural evaluation If well drained it is a good soil for various crops.

Plate 4. FAO: Humic Andosol
ST: Hydric Dystrandept
Site Lembang, Java, Indonesia.
Soil characteristics Section 3.7. This Andosol in the wet tropics at an altitude of 1250 m consists to a depth of more than 150 cm of very friable, uniform porous volcanic ash that is thixotropic (smeary) and that has a very low bulk density. The soil has an umbric A horizon (0-65 cm). Roots penetrate to a great depth, and there is a high biological activity throughout. Parent material is basic volcanic ash. The soil contains much allophane.
Agricultural elevation If terraced, these soils are excellent for many crops, including various horticultural crops. With good management, it is suitable for continuous cropping. This is one of the best soils in the tropics.

Plate 5. FAO: Ferralic Arenosol
ST: Oxic Ustipsamment
Site Niono, Mali.
Soil characteristics Section 3.8. A soil of the Sahel Zone developed in older sand dunes, consisting of fine sand. It has a weak ochric A horizon (0-22 cm) and a cambic B horizon (40-100 cm), characterized by a somewhat redder colour caused by thin iron coatings on the quartz grains (ferrugination), grading into yellowish sand.
Agricultural evaluation Suitable only for extensive grazing, because of the very long dry season and the low water-holding capacity.
Remark A quarter of the profile (on the left hand side) has been moistened in order to permit better differentiation of the soil horizons.

112

Plate 6. FAO: Humic Podzol
ST: Glossarenic Tropohumod

Site Albina, eastern Surinam.

Soil characteristics Section 3.12. This Podzol is formed in excessively drained Tertiary sand deposits. It has a coarse sandy ochric A horizon (0-24 cm), a thick (24-100 cm) albic E horizon, consisting of bleached quartz grains (light gray). There is a wavy boundary with the underlying spodic B horizon (100-155 cm), that has a dark-brown (much organic matter) upper part and a strongly brown, somewhat reddish, weakly cemented lower part. Below is the yellow coarse sand of the C horizon.

Agricultural evaluation A very poor soil, suitable only for extensive grazing. It has no agricultural potential.

Remark This soil can also be classified as an Albic Arenosol if the albic E horizon is very thick.

Plate 7. FAO: Orthic Ferralsol
ST: Quartzipsammentic Haplorthox

Site Victoria, Surinam.

Soil characteristics Section 3.13. There is an ochric A horizon (0-25 cm) over an oxic B horizon (25-155 cm), that is yellowish-red in the upper and more reddish in the lower part. The texture is sandy loam throughout the profile. Biological homogenization is intense in the upper 2 metres.

Agricultural evaluation At present forest, this soil has high potential for various crops.

Remark The soil shows all characteristics of the Typic Haplorthox except for the soil texture, which sould be sandy clay loam or finer, therefore this one is a Quartzipsammentic subgroup, indicating that it intergrades towards a Quartzipsamment.

Plate 8. FAO: Solodic Planosol
ST: Glossic Natraqualf

Site Pampas, Argentina.

Soil characteristics Section 3.14. There is an ochric A horizon (0-10 cm), an albic E horizon (10-22 cm) with hydromorphic properties, and a natric B horizon (22-60 cm) characterized by dark coatings on ped surfaces. The transition from the albic to the natric horizon is abrupt. The whitish albic material penetrates the upper part of the natric B horizon along the surfaces of columnar structured elements that have rounded tops.

Agricultural evaluation This is a grassland soil. Because of the natric B horizon, soil permeability is very low. During rainy seasons, the upper part of

113

the soil is saturated with water. It is a poor soil. Potential for agriculture is very low. (Photo and profile data: Ir G.W. van Barneveld).

Plate 9.   FAO: Calcic Xerosol
ST: Typic Calciorthid
Site Raqqa, northern Syria.
Soil characteristics Section 3.21. There is a weakly developed ochric A horizon (0-18 cm), and a distinct calcic horizon. Because of an aridic soil moisture regime (low winter rainfall), the deeper subsoil is always dry.
Agricultural evaluation Only suitable for extensive grazing; too risky for dry farming. If irrigation water is available, this soil is a very good one, for instance for cotton and wheat.

Plate 10.   FAO: Dystric Nitosol
ST: Paleustult
Site Central Ghana.
Soil characteristics Section 3.23. This soil has developed in sandstone. It has an ochric A horizon (0-40 cm) of loamy sand and an argillic B horizon (114-231 cm) of sandy clay that is characterized by a gradual smooth transition.
Agricultural evaluation At present it is a tall grass savanna, but the potential for various crops is good if farm management is improved.

Plate 11.   FAO: Ferric Acrisol
ST: Rhodic Paleudult
Site Berg en Dal, hilly land, Surinam.
Soil characteristics Section 3.24. A deep clay soil with discrete nodules of iron stone. There is a weak ochric A horizon (0-25 cm), and an argillic B horizon (38-75 cm). The soil is developed in colluvial material originating from weathering of Precambian schists in hills in the neigbourhood. The original plinthite has hardened, the soil material has been eroded, and consequently the ironstone concretions have been rounded off, and mixed with soil material. Long ago, this mixed material was deposited at the present site, and an Acrisol was formed.
Agricultural evaluation The present use is secondary forest. There is potential for grazing, not for arable crops because of susceptibility to soil erosion.

Plate 12.   FAO: Plinthite
ST: Plinthite
Site southern Victoria, Australia.

114

Characteristics Section 4.4. This plate shows plinthite in the lower part of a soil (90 to 180 cm). The red patches are plinthite, an iron-rich and humus-poor mixture of clay, quartz and other diluents. Plinthite of varying size and shape may occur in various patterns. On exposure, it changes irreversibly to irregular aggregates that are called ironstone (Plate 11). It often forms a continuous layer of hard ironstone, an ironstone hardpan (Plate 14). Plinthite is often cut into bricks that are dried in the sun; when hard, they are used for construction of walls of temples and houses. Ironstone concretions are used for paving roads. The plate shows the lower part of a Plinthic Luvisol (FAO) or Plinthic Palaeustalf (ST). Plinthite occurs all over the tropics in soils that are influenced by a fluctuating groundwater table. It is a limiting factor for crop production.

Plate 13.   FAO: Plinthic Luvisol, petroferric phase
ST: Arenic Plinthaqualf
Site   Plain in northern Ghana.
Soil characteristics   Section 3.25. The soil has a sandy loam ochric A horizon (0-36 cm), a clay loam argillic horizon (92-114 cm), and many ironstone concretions (36-114 cm) over plinthite (114-182 cm). The soil has been developed in clayey parent material of decomposed granite.
Agricultural evaluation   A poor soil, too wet in the rainy season and too dry in the dry season. Moreover it is very sandy and rooting depth is limited to the upper 60 cm by the ironstone.

Plate 14.   FAO: Chromic Luvisol
ST: Rhodic Haploxeralf
Site   southern Portugal.
Soil characteristics   Section 3.25. The soil has an ochric A horizon (0-20 cm) and a distinct argillic B horizon (45-105 cm). The deeper part of the soil is characterized by an increasing number of ironstone concretions and a real continuous ironstone hardpan (150-320 cm). The soil has all characteristics of a Rhodoxeralf, except for colour. It is probably a Xeralf developed in a former tropical soil.
Agricultural evaluation   Because of the dry summer season, this soil is only suitable for cereal winter crops, grapes and olives. If irrigation water is available, the soil is suitable for many crops.

Plate 15.   FAO: Dystric Cambisol
ST: Typic Dystropept
Site   Perica, Surinam.

Soil characteristics Section 3.26. There is an ochric A horizon (0-22 cm) of loamy fine sand, and a cambic B horizon (30-47 cm) also of loamy fine sand. The underlying C horizon has rust spots. The cambic horizon shows clearly evidence of alteration by soil profile development. This soil developed in an old beach ridge in the coastal plain.

Agricultural evaluation It has high potentials for horticultural crops, if it is well managed.

Plate 16. Sawah soil or Paddy soil

Site Bogor, Java, Indonesia.

Soil characteristics Section 3.6. It is a man-made soil, developed in volcanic ash material, as a result of continuous cultivation of irrigated rice for many decades. The soil consists of a ploughed layer (0-18 cm), that is in a stage of reduction because of continuous flooding with irrigation water, an iron-rich hardpan (25-35 cm), a manganese-rich hardpan (45-63 cm) overlying recent andesitic volcanic ash layers. Segregation, mobilization and accumulation of iron and manganese are caused by reduction in the surface soil and oxidation in the subsoil. It is a hydromorphic soil upside down.

Agricultural evaluation An excellent soil for wet rice (three crops per year are possible); however it cannot be used for other crops.

cm
— 0

— 50

Plate 1.   FAO: Dystric Fluvisol
         ST: Typic Ustifluvent

Plate 2. FAO: Orthic Solonchak
ST: Typic Salorthid

cm
— 7

— 0

— 50

Plate 3. FAO: Eutric Gleysol
ST: Typic Tropaquept

cm
— 0

— 100

Plate 4. FAO: Humic Andosol
ST: Hydric Dystrandept

cm
— 0

— 100

Plate 5. FAO: Ferralic Arenosol
ST: Oxic Ustipsamment

cm
— 0

— 100

Plate 6. FAO: Humic Podzol
ST: Grossarenic Tropohumod

cm
— 0

— 100

Plate 7. FAO: Orthic Ferralsol
ST: Quartzipsammentic Haplorthox

cm
— 0

— 50

Plate 8. FAO: Solodic Planosol
ST: Glossic Natraqualf

cm
— 0

— 50

Plate 9. FAO: Calcic Xerosol
ST: Typic Calciorthid

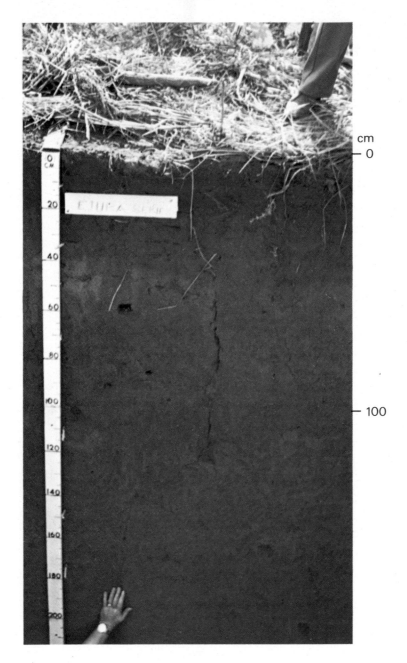

Plate 10. FAO: Dystric Nitosol
           ST: Paleustult

cm
0

100

Plate 11. FAO: Ferric Acrisol
ST: Rhodic Paleudult

cm
120 —

130 —

Plate 12.   FAO: Plinthite
            ST: Plinthite

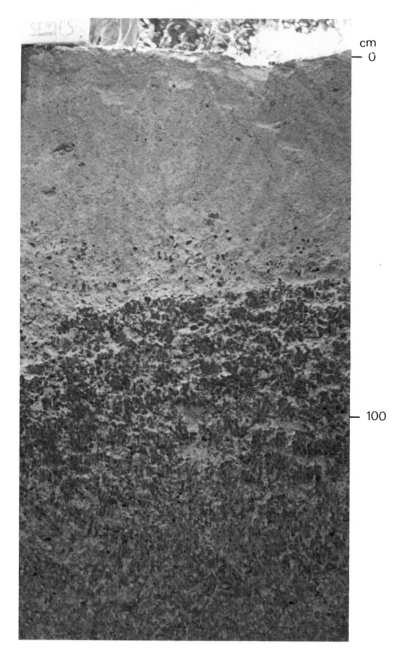

cm
— 0

— 100

Plate 13. FAO: Plinthic Luvisol
ST: Arenic Plinthaqualf

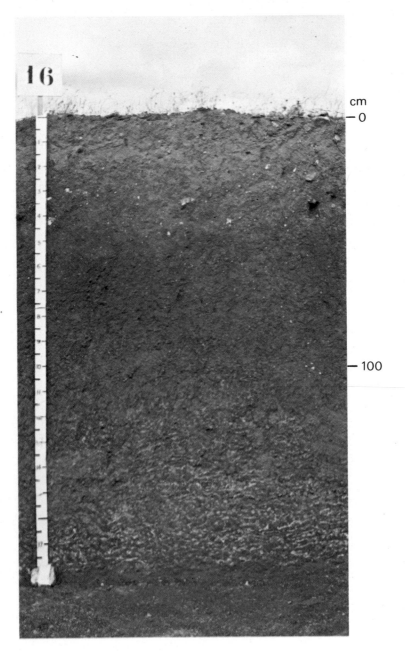

Plate 14.   FAO: Chromic Luvisol
            ST: Rhodic Haploxeralf

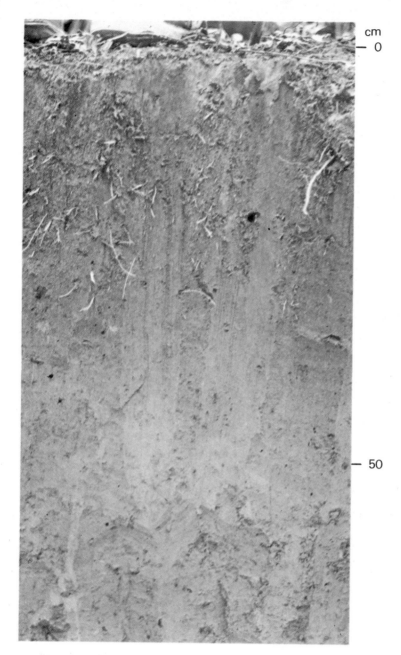

cm
— 0

— 50

Plate 15.　FAO:　Dystric Cambisol
　　　　　　ST:　　Typic Dystropept

cm
0

100

Plate 16.   FAO: Sawah soil or Paddi soil

Selected literature

Aandahl et al. (Ed), 1972. Histosols: their characteristics, classification, and use. Proceedings. Amer. Soc. of Agron., Madison, USA.

Alexander, M., 1977. Introduction to soil microbiology. Wiley, New York.

Alphen, J.G. van, F. de los Rios Romero, 1971. Gypsiferous soils. Int. Inst. of Land Recl. and Improvement, Wageningen.

Aubert, H., M. Pinta, 1977. Trace elements in soils. Elsevier, Amsterdam.

Ayers, R.S., D.W. Westcot, 1976. Water quality for agriculture. FAO, Rome. Irrigation and Drainage Paper 29.

Beek, K.J., 1978. Land evaluation for agricultural development. Int. Inst. Land Recl. and Improvement, Wageningen, Publ. No 23.

Bolt, G.H. (Ed.), 1978. Soil chemistry. Elsevier, Amsterdam.

Bornemisza, E., A. Alvarado, 1975. Soil management in tropical America. North Carolina State Univ.

Brook, R.H., 1975. Soil survey interpretation: an annotated bibliography. Int. Inst. Land Recl. and Improvement, Wageningen. – Bibliogr. 10.

Buol, S.W., F.D. Hole, R.J. McCrackers, 1979. Soil genesis and classification. 2nd revised ed. Iowa State Univ. Press, Ames.

Committee on Tropical Soils, 1972. Soils of the humid tropics. Nat. Acad. of Science, Washington.

Dregne, H.E., 1976. Soils of arid regions. Elsevier, Amsterdam.

Dudal, R., 1965. Dark clay soils of tropical and subtropical regions. FAO Rome. –FAO Devel. Paper 83.

FAO, 1970a. The preparation of soil survey reports. FAO, Rome. – Soils Bull. No 9.

FAO, 1970b.Physical and chemical methods of soil and water analysis. FAO, Rome. –Soils Bull. No 10.

FAO, 1973a. Guide to the calibration of soil tests for fertilizer recommendations. FAO, Rome. – Soils Bull. No 18.

FAO, 1973b. Calcareous soils. Seminar in Cairo, 1972. FAO, Rome. – Soils Bull. No 21.

FAO, 1973c. Catalogue of maps. Soil map of the world, 4th ed, FAO, Rome.

FAO, 1973d. Guidelines for soil profile description. 2nd ed. FAO, Rome. Also in French and Spanish.

FAO, 1976a. Second meeting of the Eastern African Sub-Committee for Soil Correlation and Land Evaluation in Ethiopia. FAO, Rome.

FAO, 1976b. Soil conservation in developing countries. FAO, Rome. – Soils Bull. No 30.

FAO, 1976c. A framework for land evaluation. FAO, Rome. – Soils Bull. No 32. Also in French and Spanish; also Publ. 22 of Int. Inst. Land Recl. and Improvement Wageningen.

FAO/Unesco, 1971-1978. Soil Map of the World, 1:5 000 000. Unesco, Paris. In two of the four following languages: English, French, Russian and Spanish. Vol. 1 Legend. Vol. 2 North America. Vol. 3 Mexico and Central America. Vol. 4 South America. Vol. 5 Europe. Vol. 6 Africa. Vol. 7 South Asia. Vol. 8 North and Central Asia. Vol. 9 South-East Asia. Vol. 10 Australia.

FAO/Unesco, 1973. Irrigation, drainage and salinity: an international source book. Unesco, Paris.

Finck, A., 1963. Tropische Böden: Einführung in die bodenkundliche Grundlagen tropischer und subtropischer Landwirtschaft. Parey, Hamburg.

Geus, J.G. de, 1973. Fertilizer guide for the tropics and subtropics. 2nd ed. Zürich.

Greenland, D.J., R.L. Chichester, (Ed.), 1977. Soil conservation and management in the humid tropics.

Hardy, F., 1970. Suelos tropicales. Mexico.

Kapagé, F.S.C.P., 1976. Tropical soils, fertility and management. Macmillan, London.

Kawaguchi, K., I.K. Kyuma, 1977. Paddy soils in tropical Asia, their material nature and fertility. Kyoto Univ. – Series No 10.

McFarlane, M.J., 1976. Laterite and landscape. Nairobi.

Mengel, K., E.A. Krikby, 1978. Principles of plant nutrition. Int. Potash. Inst., Worblaufen-Bern.

Mohr, J.E., F.A. van Baren, J. van Schuylenborgh, 1972. Tropical soils: a comprehensive study of their genesis. Mouton, The Hague.

Moorman, F., N. van Breemen, (1978). Rice: Soil, Water Land. Int. Rice Res. Inst. Los Baños.

Palmer, R.G., 1977. Introductory soil science manual. Iowa.

Papendick, R.I., P.A. Sanchez, G.B. Triplet, 1976. Multiple cropping. Amer. Soc. of Agron., Madison.

Pons, L.J., I.S. Zonneveld, 1965. Soil ripening and soil classification. Int. Inst. of Land Recl. and Improvement, Wageningen. – Publ. 13.

Proceedings, 1973. Acid sulphate soils Proceedings. Int. Symp., August 1972, Wageningen. Int. Inst. Land Recl. and Improvement, Wageningen. 2 vol – Publ. 18.

Proceeding, 1977. Soil resource inventories. Proceedings of a workshop held at Cornell University, April 1977. Cornell.

Richards, L.A. (Ed.), 1954. Diagnosis and improvement of saline and alkali soils. U.S. Dept of Agric. Washington, D.C. – Handbook 60.

Sanchez, P.A. (Ed.), 1973. A review of soils research in tropical Latin America. Raleigh, North Carolina. Also in Spanish.

Sanchez, P.A., 1976. Properties and management of soils in the tropics. Wiley, New York.

Schnitzer, M., S.U. Kahn, (Eds), 1978. Soil organic matter. Elsevier, Amsterdam.

Simonson, R.W., 1974. Non-agricultural application of soil surveys. Elsevier, Amsterdam.

Soil Science Society of America, 1978. Glossary of soil science terms. Rev. ed. Madison, USA.

Soil Survey Staff, 1951. Soil survey manual. US Dept of Agriculture, Washington, D.C.

118

Soil Survey Staff, 1975. Soil Taxonomy: a basic system of soil classification for making and interpretating soil surveys. Soil Conservation Service, US Dept of Agric., Washington, D.C. – Agriculture Handbook No 436.

Takes, Ch.A.P., 1975. Land settlement and resettlement projects: some guidelines for their planning and implementation. Int. Inst. of Land Recl. and Improvement, Wageningen. – Bull. 14.

Thomas, M.F., 1974. Tropical geomorphology. Macmillan, London.

Tisdale, S.L.; W.L. Nelson, 1975. Soil fertility and fertilizers. 3rd ed. Macmillan, New York.

UN Conference, Nairobi, 1977. Desertification: its causes and consequences. Pergamon Press, Oxford.

Vine, H., 1968. Tropical soils. – Webster & Wilson.

Vink, A.P.A., 1974. Land use in advancing agriculture. Springer, Berlin.

Wambeke, A. van, 1974. Management properties of ferralsols. FAO, Rome. – Soils Bull. 23.

Webster, R., 1977. Quantitative and numerical methods in soil classification and survey. Clarendon Press, Oxford.

Whyte, R.O., 1974. Tropical grazing lands: communities and constituent species. Junk, The Hague.

Whyte, R.O., 1976. Land and land appraisal. Dr.W. Junk b.v. Publishers, The Hague.

Young, A., 1976. Tropical soils and soil survey. Cambridge Univ. Press, Cambridge.

Some literature in French

Aubert, G., 1965. Classification des sols utilisée par la section de pédologie de l'ORSTOM. ORSTOM, Paris. – Cah. Sér. Pédol. 3.

Aubert, G. et al., 1967. Classification des sols. Édition 1967. Trav. CPCS, Grignon.

Boulaine, J., 1975. Géographie des sols. Presses Univ. de France, Paris.

Boyer, J., 1978. Le calcium et le magnésium dans les sols des régions tropicales humides et sub-humides. ORSTOM, Paris. – Int. Doc. Techn. No 35.

Duchaufour, Ph., (1976). Atlas écologique des sols du monde. Masson, Paris. (With descriptions and pictures in colour of many soils).

Duchaufour, Ph., (1977). Pédologie, 2 vol., Masson, Paris.

D'Hoore, J.L., (1964), La carte des sols d'Afrique au 1:5 000 000. Lagos.

Hénin, S., (1976-1977). Course de physique du sol. Vol. I, II, ORSTOM, Paris.

Jamagne, M., (1976). Bases et techniques d'une cartographie des sols. Inst. Nat. Res. Agron., Paris.

Magnien, R., (1969). Manuel de prospection pédologique. ORSTOM, Int. et. Doc. Techn. No. 11, Paris.

ORSTOM, (1974-1975). Les sols ferralitiques. Tombes I-IV, Paris.

ORSTOM, (1976-1978). Chronobibliographie des sols à allophane. Guadeloupe.

Segalen, P., (1973). L'aluminium dans les sols, Mémorie ORSTOM 22, Paris.

Segalen, P., (1977). La classification des sols. ORSTOM, Paris.

Sys, C. et al, (1961). La cartographie des sols au Congo, ses principes et ses méthodes. INEAC, Sér. Techn. 66, Brussels.

Vink, A.P.A., (1963). Aspects de pédologie appliquée. Baconnière, Neuchatel.

Index

124